2004 POETR

CH00967933

ONCE UPON A RHYME

IMAGINATION FOR A NEW GENERATION

Poems From South East England

Edited by Jessica Woodbridge

 Young**Writers**

First published in Great Britain in 2005 by:
Young Writers
Remus House
Coltsfoot Drive
Peterborough
PE2 9JX
Telephone: 01733 890066
Website: www.youngwriters.co.uk

SB ISBN 1 84460 669 4

Foreword

Young Writers was established in 1991 and has been passionately devoted to the promotion of reading and writing in children and young adults ever since. The quest continues today. Young Writers remains as committed to engendering the fostering of burgeoning poetic and literary talent as ever.

This year's Young Writers competition has proven as vibrant and dynamic as ever and we are delighted to present a showcase of the best poetry from across the UK. Each poem has been carefully selected from a wealth of *Once Upon A Rhyme* entries before ultimately being published in this, our twelfth primary school poetry series.

Once again, we have been supremely impressed by the overall high quality of the entries we have received. The imagination, energy and creativity which has gone into each young writer's entry made choosing the best poems a challenging and often difficult but ultimately hugely rewarding task - the general high standard of the work submitted amply vindicating this opportunity to bring their poetry to a larger appreciative audience.

We sincerely hope you are pleased with our final selection and that you will enjoy *Once Upon A Rhyme Poems From South East England* for many years to come.

Contents

Joe Hoskin (7)	32
Ned Townsend (8)	33
William James (7)	33
Thomas O'Sullivan (9)	34
Jack Sloan (8)	34
Sam Kenyon (7)	35
Eleanor Loasby (7)	35
Owen Foster (8)	36

Farnham Common Junior School, Farnham Common

Danielle Ruck (9)	36
Hayley Marriott (8)	36
Henry Gunn (8)	37
Alice Crow (8)	37
Joel Wood (8)	37
Emma Fryer (8)	38
Madeleine Northwood (8)	38
Hayley Marks (8)	39
Charlie Hewitt (9)	39
Josh King (9)	40
Hannah Jeffery (8)	40
Ella Slais (8)	41
Kristofor Stefan (8)	41
Luke Hastings (8)	42
Emma Hawkes (8)	42
Katy Fletcher (8)	43
Joseph Savage-Creighton (8)	43
Christopher Colliss (8)	43
William Hopwood (8)	44
Matthew Jewson (8)	44
George Quixley (8)	44
Alexander Tyler (8)	45
Ellie Meyer (8)	45
Luke Bentley (8)	45
Alexandra Taylor (8)	46
Harry Dymond (9)	46
James Llewelyn (8)	46
Matty Paine (8)	47
Olivia Jennings (8)	47
Alex Parkinson (8)	47
Kristie Killick (8)	48

Simran Jhooty (8)   48
Holly Holmes (8)   48
Natasha Torpy (9)   49
Harry Fernberg (8)   49
Alice Simmonds (8)   49
Harry Ray (8)   50
Darcey Yost (8)   50
Alex Bristow (8)   50
Peter Adigun (9)   51
Rosie Light (8)   51

Glory Farm CP School, Bicester

Fern Davis (8)   51
Megan Kunzer (11)   52
Ellie Andrews (8)   52
Arlo Union (10)   53
Anthony Jaggs (10)   53
Ben Blatcher (10)   54
Steven Davidson (10)   54
Siobhan Chicken (11)   55
Michael Northcott 10)   55
Shannon Bardwell (10)   56
Bethany Smith (8)   56
Rachel Walden (10)   57
Molly Lyons (7)   57
Grace Julier (8)   58
Liam Duggan (8)   58
Jamie Wilson (8)   58
Chloe Lewitt (7)   59
Liam John Barnes (7)   59
Poppy Cooper (7)   59
Harry Card (7)   60

Hawkhurst Primary School, Hawkhurst

Alec Newton (10)   60
Rowan Thomas (10)   61
Megan Smith (8)   61
Jake Barnes (9)   62
Kieran Jones (9)   62
Victoria Clayson (8)   62
Dominic Bishop (7)   63

Henry Sculley, Vincent King, Michael Gardiner & Phillip Brown (9)	63
Rachael Lloyd (9)	63
Charlotte Robinson (9)	64
Emily Morris (8)	64
Ryan Huggins (9)	65
Chloe-Mae Thorpe (8)	65
Chloë de Lullington (9)	66
Leanne Ellis (8)	66
Katie Thirkell (9)	67
Rebecca Palmer (9)	67
Harvey Daniel (8)	68
Thomas Parrish (9)	68
Robyn Matthews (9)	68
Ben Smith (9)	69
Charlotte Louise Gould (8)	69
Tyler Davies & Louis Breck (8)	69
Sarah Palmer (7)	70
Samantha Merrett (8)	70
Lauren Kerr (8)	70
Robyn Eldred (7)	71
Rosie Wood (8)	71
Jacob Collins (9)	71
Ainsley Weston (8)	72
Ryan Baker (9)	72
Bethan Eastwood (8)	72
Holly Wetherell (7)	73
Emily Wetherell (7)	73
Charlotte Clayson (8)	73
Henry Bruce (8)	74
James Cox (8)	74
Max Wood (8)	74
Adam MacKelden (7)	74

Headcorn CP School, Ashford

Sebastian Renshaw (9)	75
Danielle Groves (9)	75
Gregory Harris (9)	76
Christopher Gorman (9)	76
Alexander Warren (9)	77
Chloe Wilson (9)	77

Sarah Chattell (7)   78
Ella Buckle (8)   78
Jack Morgan (8)   78
Josie Sharp (9)   79
Tom Necci (9)   79
Grace Dickins (7)   79
Jim Owen (8)   80
Jessica Moseley (8)   80

Kings Court School, Old Windsor
Abigail Foster (8)   81
Matthew Brewis (9)   81
Ellie Welch (8)   82
George Fowler (8)   82
Aaron Stephenson (8)   82
Helena Clisby (9)   83
Ryan Whearty (8)   83
Oliver Wood (8)   83
Danni Short (7)   84
Amber Waheed (8)   84
Suhaib Riaz (9)   84
Lizzie Fielder (8)   85
Brandon Reilly (7)   85
Elicia Martin (8)   85
Aimee Cockburn (7)   86
Eisha Gandhi (8)   86
Nadiya Ziafat (7)   87
Lauren Correa (8)   87

Lewknor CE Primary School, Watlington
Gemma Sutton (7)   88
Jack McIntosh (9)   89
Isabella Carroll (7)   90
Laura Swain (7)   90
David Greensmith (8)   91
Ben McIntosh (7)   91
Thomas C S Bishop (10)   92
Dan Lamb (8)   92
Charlotte Coles (8)   92
Bella Haywood (9)   93
Jenny Claire Atterton (9)   93

Faye Baker (9)	93
Jack Hollywood (10)	94
Tom Hollywood (8)	95
Jemima Dutton (9)	95
Laura Nunn (10)	96
Amy Miles (9)	96
Adam Muttitt (9)	97
Charlotte Kotvics (10)	97
Holly Sutton (8)	98
Lily May Anson (9)	98
Megan Hawkes (9)	99
William Notley (8)	99
Elisabeth Gowens (8)	100

Longcot & Fernham CE Primary School, Faringdon

Kathryn Donnelly (8)	100
Michael Brockie (10)	101
Matthew Davis (9)	101
Philippa Sayers (8)	102
Freddie Plumb (8)	102
Ray Kimber (9)	103
Joe Timms (8)	103
Rebecca Miquel Sarjeant (9)	104
Peter Zinovieff (9)	105
Andrew Brockie (8)	106
Ellesha Bedford (9)	107
Isabel Amison (7)	107
Georgia De-Bank (8)	108
Tara Hingston (8)	108
Natascha Jane Blesing (7)	109

Long Lane Primary School, Reading

Rosie Frost (9)	109
Gregory White (8)	110
David Jones (7)	110
Jack Lowery (7)	110
Louie Sims (9)	111
Luke Dunkerton (9)	111
Megan Yeates (7)	111
Katrina Corrigan (9)	112
Rhys Frank-Harry (8)	112

William Muzzelle (7)	112
Aaron Baker (9)	113
Rachel Stout (10)	113
Benn Pickering (7)	113
Natalie Jones (9)	114
Hazel Lupton (9)	114
Tadhg Piotrowski (9)	114
Jasmine Stonehewer (9)	115
Aaron Slingsby (9)	115
Kaia Bint Savage (9)	116
Joanna Thomas (10)	116
Jodie Smith (9)	117
Alistair Haggis (9)	117
Marissa Stephens (9)	118
George Lewington (9)	118
Matthew Tuttle (9)	119

Pangbourne Primary School, Reading

Harry Oakley (7)	119
Olivia Wyndham (7)	120
Conway O'Neill (8)	120
Laura Everett (8)	121
Etham Basden (7)	121
Ryan Paxford (8)	122
Lauren Faulkner (8)	122
Amy Lafford (9)	123
Taylor Stephens (7)	123
Ella Jones (7)	124
Katherine Trew (7)	124
Scott Parker (7)	124
Michael Shellard (8)	125
Tegan Scott (7)	125
Kalila Hayward (8)	125
Joe Sumner (7)	126

Pluckley CE Primary School, Ashford

Katriona King (7)	126
Chloe Cohen (9)	127
Naomi Robinson (7)	127
Amber Hurst (8)	128
Sophie Brandon (10)	128

Emma Oliver (11)	129
Harriet Washer (10)	129
Naomi Bottle (9)	130
James Larkin (10)	130
Charlotte Tyrrell (10)	131
Megan Hill (11)	131
Sam Bridgeman (10)	132
Amy Gibbons (9)	132
Lewis Hawkes (10)	133
Christopher Wood (10)	133
Jack Barton (9)	134
Justin Bowden (9)	134
Devon Osborne (9)	135
Isobel Emblem (10)	135
Rebekah Holmes (9)	136
Daniel Hills (9)	136
Matthew Fairchild (9)	137

St Andrew's School, Reading

Michael Glenn (10)	137
Bertie Marks (10)	138
Claire Noakes (10)	138
Ysabel Brown (10)	139
Sophie Meadows (10)	139
Stuart Cummings (10)	140
Alfie Walker (10)	140

St Mary's School, Henley-on-Thames

Edward Reeve (9)	141
Benedict Turner (9)	141
Tilly Pudwell (9)	141
Jack Dent (9)	142
Emily Carr (9)	142
Anna Burrows (9)	142
Joelle Poulos (9)	143
Annie Heskin (9)	143
Kathryn Venables (10)	143
Callum Glass (9)	144

St Michael's Easthampstead CE (Aided)
Primary School, Bracknell

Catharine Ackford (7)	144
Charlie Johnson (9)	145
Emma Rowden (8)	145
Beth Seymour (8)	146
Hanna Edwards (7)	146
Lauren Owen (9)	147
Jason Slyfield (9)	147
Hayley Kennard (8)	148
Hannah Boyle (9)	148
Philippa Bowden (9)	149

Sacred Heart RC Primary School, Henley-on-Thames

Sophie Javadi-Babreh (7)	149
Callum Butler (7)	149
Dinu Popa (7)	150
Daniel Cridland (8)	150
Myfanwy Mountford (7)	151
Callum Hilton (7)	151

Sandwich Junior School, Sandwich

Oliver Mackinnon (10)	152
Jack Venner (10)	153
Thomas Skirrow (10)	154
Alex Cowan (10)	155
Jessica Dymott (10)	156
Adam Cox (10)	157
David Hands (10)	158
Katherine Belsey (8)	159
Taylor Smith (10)	160
Adam Pope (10)	161
Chloe Cole (9)	162
Christina Page (9)	162
James Igglesden (8)	163
Rachel Barclay (9)	163
Elliott Burns (8)	164
Grant Hammet (9)	165
Hannah Breddy (8)	166
Bradley Marsh (10)	166

Harry Sampson (9)   167
Lisa Harrison (9)   167
William Bedford (9)   168
John Sandy-Hindmarch (9)   168
Erin Gilham (9)   169
Jordan Maclaurin (9)   169
Elizabeth Stowell (8)   170
Matilda Scott-Neve (8)   170
Helen Jarvis (9)   171
Gareth Williams (8)   171
Harriet Jackson (8)   172
Kirstie Carless (9)   172
Jade Mosley (8)   173
Charlotte Kenton (8)   173
Joshua Relton (8)   174
William Mellin (8)   174
Andrew Kirby (8)   175
Matthew Sharman (8)   175
William French (10)   176
Marc Young (10)   176
Natasha Westwood (10)   177
Naomi Ward (10)   177
Joe Wheeler (10)   178
Jade Gothard (10)   178
Jordan Green (10)   179
Jack Barber (10)   179
Daisy Kemp (8)   180
Benjamin Cockram (10)   180
Robert Kirby (10)   181
Michael Jarrett (10)   181
Rebecca Chamberlain (10)   182
Hannah Knowler (10)   183
Vivienne Hayles (11)   184
Hannah Trew (8)   184
Charlye Hodgkins-Hale (8)   185
Holly Groombridge (10)   185
Rosie Charter (10)   186
Becky Brisley (9)   186
Abigail Greenfield (9)   187
Tom Rigden (9)   187
Chloé Forsyth (9)   188
Lauren Maw (10)   189

Kate Lyden (10)	190
Dan O'Brien (11)	190
Dominika Szücsová (10)	191
Chelsea Cox (10)	191
Samantha Martin (10)	192
Rosie Beale (9)	192
Ellen Hall (9)	193
Bethany Gibson (8)	193
Rachel Collins (10)	194
Megan Reeve (8)	194
Fraser Meldrum (8)	195
Sophie Kennett (8)	195
Elliot Torbett (10)	196
David Buckmaster (10)	196
Gabrielle Quinn (10)	197
Sam Bean (10)	197
Hannah Taylor (8)	198
Brennan Westwood (8)	199
Georgia Down (8)	200
Stacey Cornwall (10)	200
Laura Roscoe (10)	200
Simon Malhomme (8)	201
Jacob Burslem (8)	201
Emily Harris (10)	201
Christopher Arman (10)	202
Abigail Harrop (10)	203
Shafaye Abbot (8)	204
Harry Lawrence (8)	204
Heather Godfrey (8)	204
Ryan Tench (8)	205
Lauren Beale (8)	205
Dominic Pettit (9)	205
Jack Brown (9)	206
Robert Holbrook (8)	206
Ben Skirrow (9)	207
Peter Turay (9)	207
Rebecca Sullivan (9)	208
Charlie Skinner (9)	208
Lydia Sinnett-Smith (9)	209
Ryan Brown (9)	209
Michael Jones (10)	210
Eve Batts (9)	210

Jason Clayton (10)   211
Jack Butcher (9)   211
Rebecca Reynolds (10)   212
Jemma Lowley (10)   213
Jade Beale (9)   214
Ellie Powling (9)   214
Siân Benzies (9)   215

South Ascot Village School, Ascot
Omid Rajabalipour (10)   215
Prerna Kapoor (11)   216
Liam Kennedy (10)   216
Nicholas Wiggett (10)   217
Callum Mitchell (10)   217
Lewis Cornwall (10)   218
Fraser Morby (10)   218
Louella Fox (10)   219
Reece Merryman (10)   220
Andre Jotle (10)   220
Christopher Reeves (10)   220
Mille Roche (10)   221
Rebecca Taylor (10)   221

Stanton Harcourt CE Primary School, Witney
Katie Ray (8)   221
Kyle Luckett (8)   222

Stoke Poges Primary School, Slough
Robert Ford (9)   222
Bethan Nankivell (8)   223
Naveen Mahil (7)   223
Lewis Howell (7)   224
Cara Waite (7)   225
Verity Kyley (10)   225
Mishalle Iqbal (10)   226
Jasmine Jalif (10)   226
Baveena Heer (9)   227
Faye Bovington (8)   227
Aneesha Mahil (9)   228
Nikita Saggar (9)   228

Charlie Hertel (9)	229
Rabiah Khalid (9)	229
Aikta Sharma (9)	230
Taylor Nelmes (7)	230
Ryan Lalli (7)	231
Amarjit Mann (10)	231
Hannah Delderfield (9)	232
Amy Benton (8)	232
Manraj Brar (8)	233
Louise Pocock (9)	233
Malaika Kingue (9)	234
Megan Picot (8)	234
Marianna Geany (9)	235
Rebecca Holliday (9)	235
Simran Gill (8)	235
Harjoth S Bahra (10)	236
Laiqah Ramzan (7)	236

Woodcote Primary School, Woodcote

Gabrielle Bianco (8)	237
Bethany Smith (9)	237
Katie Thorne (7)	238
Chloe Anderson (9)	238
Anke-Katerina Andrews (10)	239
Emma Barrett (10)	239
Genevieve Simpson (9)	240
Kelly-Violet Draper (10)	241
Ellie Brown (9)	241
Matthew Norman (10)	241
Baitong Namasonthi (9)	242

The Poems

Funny Gran

My gran is as old as a dinosaur
Her laugh is like a kookaburra
She walks like a tortoise
She drives as if she is in a bumper car
Her hair is as white as clouds
She is always as cold as polar bears without any skin on
But the best thing about Gran is when she tells interesting,
                                                    funny stories.

Anonymous

New Buildings

New buildings, new buildings!
With nice carpets blue,
New toilets, new classrooms,
But still not much glue.
Thank goodness we won't meet our doom.

New buildings, new buildings!
Remember our old school
With those oh so small mobiles
I'm sad we don't have a pool
At least we don't have to walk miles.

New buildings, new buildings!
We're growing a new field,
We've got a new playground
At least it's not peeled.
Thank goodness it doesn't make a sound.

New buildings, new buildings!
The builders have worked hard
I think they should have a week off
I wonder if they used lard
I think they used a cloth.

Ricky Rolfe (9)
Aldington CP School, Ashford

From The Car To School

Driving up Forge Hill all three of us,
my brother, sister and I are waiting excitedly
wanting to see inside the new school building
not knowing what to expect.

Our mum parks the car.
We get out of it, quickly,
forgetting a lunch box, because we are all too giggly and fidgety.
All trying to get out of one door isn't very easy!

We stand on the newly painted playground
talking to friends unseen for weeks, catching up
from when you last saw them.

At last Mrs Shears-Warren calls us in.
It is like going into a totally new school:
a bit strange really, even with all of your old friends.

Olivia Unsworth-Brown (10)
Aldington CP School, Ashford

Aldington School

Come and see, come and gaze in amazement at our new school,
Look at the screaming on our new playground
Look at the new grass growing for our new field.

Come and see, come and gaze in amazement at our new school,
Come and see the teachers, proud of what they have done
Come and see the matching blue corridors.

Come and see, come and gaze in amazement at our new school,
Come and see Class 4, that is in the old hall.

Come and see, come and gaze in amazement at our new school,
Come and see the children working hard in their new classrooms.

Thomas Burtonwood (9)
Aldington CP School, Ashford

New Building

When I entered the new school building
I felt like I was under a spell.
It was amazing how much the school had changed
and how much the builders dealt with.

But there is still lots of happy memories about the old school.
We must remember that the old school wasn't a tatty, uncared building
because it is still in a special place in our hearts.

All the classes are all neat, tidy, big, wide,
spacious, comfortable and cosy.

The corridors with more space to walk,
but to everybody it is a place to talk.

To finish off, the toilets are cleaner.
Compared to the old ones they are like shiny gold
so now Mrs Gosbee would not have to do as much work
as she used to do and now all the cleaning
things in the shops would not be sold.

Carlton Robinson (9)
Aldington CP School, Ashford

The First Day Back

When the sun is shining and I'm back at school,
I realise it was very cool when I walked through the corridor,
I had a tour to find my way around the school
if I hadn't there would be war.

When the sun is shining and I walked through the door,
I saw Class 4.

When the sun is shining and I walked through the door,
I knew it would be hard, it would be harder than a tour.

When the sun is shining and I walked through the door,
I thought the hall was bigger than a purple dinosaur.

Beth Hodges (9)
Aldington CP School, Ashford

Autumn Song

At autumn song everyone sang along.
Hedgehogs bustle, trees rustle,
and their leaves brush the whole world's face.
Fires burning, chimney tops spraying
their smoke all over the town.

Dan Johannsen (6)
Aldington CP School, Ashford

Modern Daffodils

I walked quickly down the street
Where nowhere was there a hill
When there in front of me I met
A little, yellow daffodil.
Motorbikes and cars whizzed past
Planes above went really fast.

The next day I was sat at home
Watching the TV
When I was sat there all alone
The daffodil popped up at me,
The daffodil came through the door
That led on into the store.

The waves danced almost all day
When I was by the sea,
Sometimes I thought they'd dance away
Then the daffodil sat next to me,
The sun was shining bright and hot
I didn't know whether to get an ice cream or not.

The swimming pool is open at last
But while I was waiting outside
The daffodil came walking past
And went down the water slide,
Many adventures but surprise, surprise
The daffodil got wet and died.

Hannah Stokes (10)
Batt CE Primary School, Witney

The Sea

It waves its glossy white waves over the strong, bumpy cliffs.
It pulls fish in and out with the tide coming close to the soft, yellow sand
Its creatures run and hide from our great, big feet.
As the wide sea opens its wide mouth to swallow anything available.
The creatures scatter the wide sea floor to hunt for its lush, tasty prey.
The sea enters the ocean.
The ocean is wide, it covers nearly the whole wide, wonderful world.
The ocean's great big creatures eat almost anything
Like the gigantic, great, white shark that eats small fish
Like salmon, tuna and lots more.
Whales live in the beautiful ocean.
They eat lots and lots of krill.
As you go further south and north
Ice bergs scour the entire ocean.

Sophie Nobes & Michaela Paish (8)
Batt CE Primary School, Witney

My Year 6 Trip To Bude in Cornwall

On Monday was fencing with big, funny masks,
Next was Cluedo with lots of questions to ask.

On Tuesday was canoeing with really cool boats,
Now was beach games, making sandcastles with moats.
Last was Egg Destroyer.

On Wednesday was surfing with really big waves,
Next was IE and archery with some of my faves.
Last was It's A Knockout.

On Thursday was blind trail which was really muddy,
Next was orienteering for which you needed a buddy.
Last was the disco.

Today is *Friday,* we have to go home.
We did a team challenge which we didn't do alone.

Tilly Haley (10)
Batt CE Primary School, Witney

The Candy House

Opening the gingerbread door,
Feet resting on a glazed, candy floor
A coat rack made from a thin chocolate stick
Oh how I wish I could take a lick

Running up the liquorice stairs
Marshmallow cushions on the lollipop chairs
Looking at the beds with the candyfloss covers
Perfect for the sweethearted and lovers

Jelly bean lights glittering on the wall
Piles of toffee reach up tall
But sadly this is just one of my dreams
My real house is made of peppermint creams!

Eleanor Beadle (10)
Batt CE Primary School, Witney

Nature

See the lambs galloping by
Look up into the deep blue sky
Can you see the golden sun?
Can you see the children eating their iced-pink buns?
Can you see the ripe fruits grow?
Can you see the meadows glow?
Can you see the swishing trees?
Can you see the bright blue breeze?
Can you see the cows far away?
Can you see the break of day?
Now you've seen all these things
You can enjoy how the blue tits sing.

Rebecca Pau (7)
Batt CE Primary School, Witney

Deep In The Jungle

Deep in the jungle where nobody knows
A big fat hippo swimming in the river.

Deep in the jungle where nobody knows
A stripy, poisonous snake slithering in the jungle.

Deep in the jungle where nobody knows
A monkey is swinging in the trees.

Deep in the jungle where nobody knows
An elephant is stomping through the jungle.

Deep in the jungle where nobody knows
A big, fierce lion . . . *roars!*

Kristian Rutenberg-Houchen (8)
Batt CE Primary School, Witney

The Black Cat

It was a dark and cold night,
the moon was whole and the stars were bright.
A black cat tiptoed as if in fright,
its prey quivering in the night.
The cat's eyes turned the colour of deepest night,
he knew its prey was now in sight.
The cat's eyes turned the colour of steel,
knowing that he would catch his meal.
The cat leapt, the prey ran away
and knew it would live another day.
The cat retired beneath the stars
awaiting its next prey, but maybe not today!

Emily Grant (9)
Batt CE Primary School, Witney

Swim, Swim, Swim

As I swim, swim, swim,
I kick my feet, feet, feet,
I think about my stroke, stroke, stroke,
About my arms, arms, arms.

I wonder how many strokes I've done, done, done,
Argh, I can't think, think, think,
Someone's behind me tumble turn and out again.

Phew, I sorted that out,
Oh no! Got to go *quick, quick, quick,*
Wow, I think I've won, *yes I have!*

Martha Horan (9)
Batt CE Primary School, Witney

What Friends Are For

Friends share with you
Friends look out for you
Friends play with you
Friends respect you
So everyone needs friends.

Shannon Baker, Rhiannon Truby (8) & Stella Ryley (7)
Batt CE Primary School, Witney

Teddies

Teddies are sweet in the most delightful way.
From here to there they shout hooray!
From bear to bird, from bird to rat, from rat to cat
From cat to dog they all have life.
When the day is done, me and my teddies
Snuggle up and teddies bring good luck.

Rebecca Woods (9)
Batt CE Primary School, Witney

Dolphin

In the deep blue sea
Right in front of me
I saw a big, grey fin
Of a common dolphin.

In the deep blue sea
While having my tea
A dolphin rose up
And drank from my cup.

In the deep blue sea
The dolphin remembered me
Now I am remembering
The big bottle-nosed dolphin.

Lorelle Colleton (8)
Batt CE Primary School, Witney

A Little Eye

There was a little eye
Who lived in the sky.
He jumped up and down,
And had a little frown.
That strange little eye
Who lived in the sky.

Joanna Stubbs (8)
Batt CE Primary School, Witney

Horses

Prancing and dancing around a field,
Eating grass and neighing loudly
Swaying their heads backwards and forwards
Ponies running to their mothers
On a summer's day.

Francesca Marks (8)
Batt CE Primary School, Witney

Birthdays

Birthdays are cool!
Birthdays are fun!
Birthdays are had by everyone!
You may have a party!
You may have a cake!
Birthday cards sometimes come in the post!
Friends come to your parties sometimes!
You get presents from your friends!

Annabel Nash (8)
Batt CE Primary School, Witney

Time In The Trenches

Time in the trenches
Down below in the mud,
Covered in blood, red blood
Dead bodies cover the ground.
Germans, *no,* a trench they have found
Ammunition is in short supply,
Armies by armies, countries comply
Time is not fun in the trenches.

Finn Ryley (10)
Batt CE Primary School, Witney

My Best Friend

Why don't you look at me?
We always disagree.
I know I'm always right
But you always want to fight.
Let's just be friends, OK
Don't turn that way!
Crash!
I Told you.

Joslyn Beadle & Tilly Maddocks (7)
Batt CE Primary School, Witney

Skateboarding

Dad thinks he can skateboard,
Mum thinks she can too,
But the only person about
Who this is true - *is me!*
My parents are so embarrassing
When they take me to the skateboard park
They don't like sharing and taking turns
And we're there until it's nearly dark
Really the only person who should be skateboarding
Is me!

James Tudge (7)
Batt CE Primary School, Witney

Person, Place, Time, Weather

The detective strolled grumpily down the creepy, dark street.
It was as cold as ice.
The rain was thundering down.
Suddenly his flashlight stopped.
He fell into a dark, gloomy hole.
He landed on something hard, it was a pile of dead bodies.

Eric Hall (10)
Charlbury Primary School, Chipping Norton

Puddle Of Blood

In Manchester at 5pm
The detective was gradually strolling down the abandoned alley
The rain slopping down into his face.
He came to a puddle of blood
He took some of the blood in a syringe
He went back below to his office
To work out the mystery.

Tasmin Duester (10)
Charlbury Primary School, Chipping Norton

Mysterious Bobby

Mysterious Bobby
The best detective in town.
He was about to solve another murder
He could hardly be seen
Under his long, thick, black coat
In the shadows of Cringey Street
In the suburbs of Manchester.
'I need a hot bath
I need a hot bath,'
He moans.
He was out in a gale and in the rain,
There he was, the person he had been looking for.
Bill Bandit's the serial killer, 'He must be the killer.'
The blood on his knife was the same DNA as the victim's blood.
Murder solved - 5pm 15th September.

Freddie Hammond (10)
Charlbury Primary School, Chipping Norton

Guernica By Picasso

The shouts and screams of women and children,
Screeching, wounded animals,
Galloping around in a rage,
A woman screaming, a bone-chilling scream at the ceiling,
Mourning for her dead son, lying draped in her arms,
Victims trying to escape from the rubble,
Dead men being kicked to one side by civilians running for cover,
Stunning heads lying detached,
A cut arm and a shattered sword,
The chaos of Guernica should always be remembered.

Omar McCutcheon (11)
Charlbury Primary School, Chipping Norton

White

White makes me think of snow falling down,
Like a thick layer of white dust,
The kind that covers the town,
I just must . . .
Say . . .
White makes me think of the hair on my nana,
The whiteness of a snowman,
The white-yellow colour of a banana,
The plain paper of an unmade plan.
White makes me think of leaping lambs running in the grass,
The fluffy candyfloss
Sheep grazing in the pass
And the white from lip gloss.

Charley Currie (9)
Faringdon Junior School, Faringdon

What Is Black?

Black is a shadow, black is a cat
Black is the night containing a bat
Black is a cauldron being stirred by a wizard
Black is a storm and the middle of a blizzard
Black is a hole that is misty at night
Black is a bruise that is such a sight
Black is a panther prowling around
Black is a note that makes a loud sound
Black is gloomy, there's no doubt about it
But can you image a world without it?

Oliver Attwood (10)
Faringdon Junior School, Faringdon

The Red Of Everything

The red of betrayal and anger,
The red of the Devil who persuades us to slander,
The red of the setting sun,
The red of the cherry on a bun,
The red of embarrassment when you've said something wrong,
The red of a camp fire around which we sing songs,
The red of blood, despatched from a vein,
The red of suffering and of pain,
The red of deceit and villainy,
The red of rage and of felony,
Red is the source of everything,
From ketchup to a ruby ring.

Josh Smedley (11)
Faringdon Junior School, Faringdon

Red Is . . .

The sun setting as I sit on top of the hill
A volcano erupting as people watch in amazement
A rose sitting in the front window
The foods people love: cherry, beetroot, tomatoes and strawberries
Love and romance on Valentine's Day
Embarrassment as my dad tells an old story about me
My blood as it rushes through my veins, scarlet and ruby-red
A sunburned back as it crisps in the heat
Danger, a sign as I walk up the mountain
A demon as he sends people to Hell
Anger as I get mad at people
The open fire as I sit in the living room
Red is truly a brilliant colour.

Liam Farmer (10)
Faringdon Junior School, Faringdon

Red

A swarm of children walking to the infants school
        Red
My mum's face when she's angry
        Red
A bowl of luscious strawberries covered with cream
        Red
A juicy apple waiting to be bitten into
        Red
A sunburnt nose after laying in the sun too long
        Red
The stained fingers after picking berries
        Red
A bright red Manchester United sweater
        Red!

Tamara Williams (10)
Faringdon Junior School, Faringdon

White Seems To Be

The snow on a cold day in winter,
My clean carpet from the carpeter
The stick of school chalk on the board,
The bleach people use on an ancient hoard.
The colour of my best friend's dog,
The cleanest ever winter hog.
The colour of the paper I'm writing on now,
The shade of the splodges on a cow.
The fluffy clouds rolling by
My paper aeroplane somewhere up high
Lambs frolicking and jumping around
A baby's pyjamas when it's sleeping sound.

Freya Watson (10)
Faringdon Junior School, Faringdon

The Witch Spell For Trouble

Number one is a baby's lung,
Drop in a long chameleon's tongue.
Put in a tousled, grey horse mane
Slop in a lumpy and wriggly old rotting brain
From the morning a screaming baby's wail
Plop in a brown, ingrowing nail.

Simmer and boil, blacken like oil
Cauldron bubble, send trouble and toil!

Add in a teaspoon of a teacher's moan
Pour in half a bottle of granny's groan.
As disgusting as it may seem
This spell is a witch's dream
Also a slippery, silver shark's fin
Plus a lippy, filthy grin.

Simmer and boil, blacken like oil
Cauldron bubble, send trouble and toil!

Jess Kenyon (9)
Faringdon Junior School, Faringdon

Red

Murderous rage that's what red is.
Blood from a murdered animal.
Anger that's what it is.
When your face turns red
And steam leaks out of your ears
That's what red is.
Red is the colour of love
When Cupid's arrow hits you
That's when it starts.

Jacob Reid (9)
Faringdon Junior School, Faringdon

My Grandparents

G randparents are great when they give you treats
Yum yum!
R eally boring jokes but you laugh because they are so bad!
Ha, ha!
A ll of them tall or small, I love them all
Love, love, love!
N aughty, nice, sugar, spice!
Sugar, spice, sugar, spice!
D rying dishes, they are so good at that.
Soap, soap, soap!
P ennies and pounds all around
Pennies, pennies, pennies!
A mazing people they surely are.
Great, great, great!
R ound the town they slowly walk.
Slow, slow, slow!
E ndless stories about the war.
Boom, boom, boom!
N ever miss bingo on Friday night!
Bingo, bingo, bingo!
T hey are absolutely fab.
Fab, fab, fab!
S omebody to look forward to seeing.
See, see, see!

Megan Palmer (10)
Faringdon Junior School, Faringdon

Gold

Little pinches of glitter sprinkling happiness
Melted butter on toast on a cold winter's eve
Great riches and money from a palace in the mountains
Or the gold of pure power, wearing the crown
The magic of stars on a velvet background
Gold, health and life.

Jack Porter (10)
Faringdon Junior School, Faringdon

What Is Blue?

Blue is the ocean swirling and rough
Blue is a sadness when you've had enough.
Blue is a loyalty, a fragment of ice,
Sometimes blue is a friend being nice.
Blue are your tears when you are upset
Blue is a whisper so not to forget.
Blue is coldness that builds up inside
When you are crying because someone has died.
Tide in, tide out, it is so true
And when your emotions take over
Running through your veins will be blue.
Blue is the bright sky, a sweet-singing bird
Blue is United though nobody's heard.
Blue is a flower, blue is a tear
Blue is a song that sounds so near.
Blue is a tiny piece of our life
Blue is of shyness not of strife.
Blue is a cool colour do not forget it
There is no way there would be life without it.

Hannah Westall (10)
Faringdon Junior School, Faringdon

Orange

The sun setting on a calm day
The sun's amazing rays
Maybe a very stripy tiger
Maybe the dashing flames of fire
Orange reminds me of a spicy tang
Orange reminds me of the vibes of a big, loud bang
Maybe you will be quite a whiz
When you really know what orange is.

Maggi-May Saunders-Williams (10)
Faringdon Junior School, Faringdon

Grandparent Alphabet

A is for amazing
B is for brainy
C is for cautious
D is for dozy
E is for entertaining
F is for funny
G is for generous
H is for happy
I is for interesting
J is for joker
K is for kind
L is for lively
M is for magnificent
N is for noble
O is for orderly
P is for priceless
Q is for quietly
R is for respectful
S is for skilful
T is for terrific
U is for unique
V is for victorious
W is for wonderful
X is for exciting
Y is for young
Z is for zealous

Now you've learnt your grandparent alphabet
All these words are describing them.

James Campbell (10)
Faringdon Junior School, Faringdon

The Three Witches

Round the cauldron we go
In goes the rotten limb as well as a scorpion's sting
Bloodsucking leeches, don't forget the rotten peaches.
An old man's dead skin and some dead bodies from a bin
Double, double, make it bubble, let it burn and let it bubble.
Remember the baby's cry and the helpless pig's eye
Chuck in the spider's hair and the entrails of a bear
Don't forget the elephant's eye and the rotten pig pie
Double, double, make it bubble, let it burn and let it bubble.

Louis Bouwers (10)
Faringdon Junior School, Faringdon

Blue

A trickling stream going through the forest
Little square ice cubes melting on a plate
A miserable person sobbing and crying
A big blue jumper ready to go in the washing
A wonderful, shiny butterfly flying from flower to flower,
A huge, sparkling sea with boats floating across
A freezing cold water bottle ready to be drunk.

Heather James (9)
Faringdon Junior School, Faringdon

Daisy

A daisy has a pretty face,
Her petals white as snow,
I think I know the very place,
My daisy likes to grow . . .
What a pretty daisy flower
Sitting in the grass
Waiting for the rain to show
And the clouds to pass . . .

Louisa Shaw (8)
Faringdon Junior School, Faringdon

Black

The colour of a dark soul
Darker than coal
When mice scuttle around
When moles go underground
A pit of shame
While everyone says you're lame
Black cats sit around a blazing fire
Blank TV sitting alone in an empty house
A black rat fighting a mouse
Black is the darkest night
So don't get a fright!

Daisy Green (9)
Faringdon Junior School, Faringdon

Grandad

G reat at cooking
R eally good at tricks
A good joker
N ice at swimming
D rive around together
A nice grandad
D oes things with me.

Matthew Edmunds (9)
Faringdon Junior School, Faringdon

Sleepy Old Fred

There once was a man called Fred
Who liked to stay in bed
He had a big hiccup
Which made him wake up
Then he noticed his big head.

James Doleman (7)
Faringdon Junior School, Faringdon

My Granny Annie

My granny Annie is very grotty
She only just stopped using a potty.
She gets lots of cash
For her killer moustache.
She still plays with dollies and shopping trolleys.
Often she dresses as a flamingo
And goes and cheats at bingo.
Once she won a pink teddy bear
She then tried to hypnotise it
With her petrifying stare.
My granny Annie is 110
And sometimes she goes mad and clucks like a hen.
But I'm sure when she's gone and dead
She definitely won't stay in bed.

Oliver Billson (10)
Faringdon Junior School, Faringdon

If

If you could be kind to every child around
If you could bend over so you could see the ground
If you could not go grotty then everyone will like you
If you could change your name maybe Tia or Sue?

Don't tell lies or you'll be a fibber
It's OK to be a chicken but always be a giver.

If you could be young and active all day long
If you had hair like Elvis and always sing his songs.
If you could play bingo and always win the game
If you could stand on your own feet and never feel ashamed.

Then you, my friends, are the perfect grandparents.

Elizabeth Fry (10)
Faringdon Junior School, Faringdon

The Extraordinary Dog

I am The Extraordinary Dog
I don't eat meat, dog food or bones
I chomp and chew and gulp and gobble:
      cherry pancakes
      zebra pie
      rhino pudding
I don't walk on four feet, jump or pounce
I walk on two feet and I slide on the floor like the wind.
I don't bark or growl,
I giggle, shout, scream
And howl, hiss and whisper!

I am The Extraordinary Dog!

Max Waymark (7)
Faringdon Junior School, Faringdon

The Marvellous Butterfly

I am The Marvellous Butterfly!
I don't eat nectar or bugs
I spit and squash and gobble:
      chewy bugs
      smelly treacle
      and chocolate raspberries
I don't fly, flutter or sing
I jump like a kangaroo
And dive in cool, deep water.
I don't flap or flop
I honk and snort!
And whistle like the wind.
I am The Marvellous Butterfly!

Beth Clarke (7)
Faringdon Junior School, Faringdon

What Is Black?

Black is a shadow, black is the night
Black is despair and black is fright.
Black is deadly, black is sly
Black is a Ninja with the keenest of eyes.
Black is dead, black is here
Black is something that lurks and leers.
Black is a hole, black is a cat,
Black is a wizard with a tall, pointed hat.

Black is a cauldron, black is space
Black is darkness, right up in your face.
Black is a witch flying high in the sky
Black is useful for an undercover spy.
Black is a nightmare stuck in your head
Ready to flash when you go to bed.

Charlie Lowers (10)
Faringdon Junior School, Faringdon

The Extremely Marvellous Magpie!

I am The Extremely Marvellous Magpie
I don't eat fish, worms or eggs . . .
I chew and gulp and gobble
Smelly glasses, stinky eyeballs, mouldy socks!
I don't fly or scuttle
I pounce quickly and I leap from tree to tree
I don't squeak or squawk
I growl and purr
And I whistle like the clouds
I am The Extremely Marvellous Magpie!

Barnaby Vogt (7)
Faringdon Junior School, Faringdon

The Extraordinary Dog

I am The Extraordinary Dog,
I don't eat meat, bones or biscuits,
I chomp and chew and gulp and gobble:
> Banana flavour
> Sausages
> Apple chips.
> Strawberry bricks.
I don't walk on four legs, run or leap,
I hop and I jump like a dancing Indian.
I laugh like a monkey.
I growl like a spaniel,
And I squeal like a bird.

I am The Extraordinary Dog!

Briony Lynn (8)
Faringdon Junior School, Faringdon

The Extraordinary Eagle

I am The Extraordinary Eagle!
I don't eat meat, dead things or eggs
I scrunch and crunch on:
> electric burgers,
> spider pie,
> stinky teacher crumble.
I don't fly, peck or flap
I bob up and down on the sea like a jellyfish
And zoom in the air like an aeroplane
I don't squawk or screech
I snort, wail and I scream like a tornado.
I am The Extraordinary Eagle!

Sebastian Allum (7)
Faringdon Junior School, Faringdon

The Mexican Flipper

There was a Mexican flipper,
Who had a Chihuahua as a nipper,
The Mexican flipper ripped his work,
He rapped all night
Tickles and frights.
He flipped a pancake
Also ached all night.
The Chihuahua was a bright fright
Would it bite?
So the flipper flipped,
As soon as he tripped.
He flipped lots of stuff,
A man said, 'Tough!'
He flipped the Chihuahua.
Whose name is Baba
But the flipper was a gripper.

Victoria Taylor (8)
Faringdon Junior School, Faringdon

The Thoughtless Dog

I am The Thoughtless Dog!
I don't eat meat or drink water . . .
                I gulp and gulp and suck up
                green pencil cases
                blue pens
                brown rubbers.
I don't run, leap or play
I sit and think seriously
And fly like a sparrowhawk!
I don't woof or growl
I yell, I yodel, I holler and screech like an owl
I am The Thoughtless Dog!

Joe Butcher (8)
Faringdon Junior School, Faringdon

The Extraordinary Dog

I am The Extraordinary Dog
I don't eat bones, meat or dog food
I crunch, gobble and gulp:
> chicken wallpaper
> strawberry leaves
> raspberry pencil cases
I don't run, walk and jump
I juggle like a clown, leap like a frog
And dance like a gymnast.
I don't drink water or milk
I drink hot chocolate, chicken coffee and kangaroo tea.
I don't bark or whine
I mumble, grumble and neigh like a horse
I am The Extraordinary Dog.

Ben Elliott (8)
Faringdon Junior School, Faringdon

My Grandad

Grandad is as technical as a robot,
He likes lying down when it's hot,
But he never burns his bot,
When we go out shopping
He buys me a bun, yum, yum,
And he's tons and tons of fun,
He brightens up my day
And he will pay for the pennies we spend
He plays swingball with me
Then we have tea
Then I will go to bed sleepy from the day
I love grandad so much
It's so hard to give him up.

Hugh Jones (8)
Faringdon Junior School, Faringdon

The Woolly Mammoth

His beautiful woolly coat
Covers him like a blanket,
It's brown and heavy
His trunk's grey and moves up, down, left and right.
As he trudges through the ages
His ears hear for miles
As they flap in the wind
They look like they're torn at the side.
The Woolly Mammoth.

Holly Vanags (8)
Faringdon Junior School, Faringdon

Green

Green is the grass, green is a leaf
Green is a turtle in a coral reef.
Green is a snake, twisting and winding
Green is an island someone is finding.
Green is a friend, fresh and new
Green is a grasshopper on the morning dew.
Green is feeling jealous when you are down
Green is loud and jewels on a crown!

Shauna Doyle (10)
Faringdon Junior School, Faringdon

Fun

Fun is pink like candyfloss
Just a bit like my lip gloss
Like frost with snow when it falls
Snow makes the frost on the walls
When it's sunny, the rainbow's out
We put skirts and shorts on and then we shout!

Emily Stepp (7)
Faringdon Junior School, Faringdon

The Darkness

I am standing in an alleyway
Hear, fear, shudder, tear.
It is as black as the night
Hear, fear, shudder, tear.
I am walking around in circles
Hear, fear, shudder, tear.
I can hear the birds singing softly to the baby birds
Hear, fear, shudder, tear.

Mollie Eltham (8)
Faringdon Junior School, Faringdon

Anger

Anger is red and orange like a fiery sun.
It sounds like steam from a train and hot, red fire.
It feels like an earthquake in your mind.
It tastes like red-hot fire burning down a house.
It looks like steam coming from your ears.
It smells like a fireball.
It reminds me of a bonfire.

Emily Peer (8)
Faringdon Junior School, Faringdon

My Nan Is . . .

My nan is as kind as a bird.
My nan is as funny as a clown.
My nan is as caring as a nurse.
My nan is as wise as an owl.
My nan is as fast as a cheetah.
My nan's hair is as grey as an elephant.

Andrew Prescott (7)
Faringdon Junior School, Faringdon

My Grandparents

My grandparents, although they're old are still fun
And every time they take me out they buy my favourite bun.
They are so great, they take me out to places like the zoo
They give me loads of great advice and tell me what to do.
I love hearing stories of my dad when he was small
But now he's rather old and he is really rather tall.
They are clever too and funny as old barn owls
They always run to me when they hear me howl!

Beth Porter (8)
Faringdon Junior School, Faringdon

My Grandad

My grandad is the spark in my life
He brightens up my day
When I ask him for advice
He tells me what to say
Whenever we go round
He carves marzipan into things
And whenever he finds out something
He just gives us a ring.

Alexander Robinshaw (8)
Faringdon Junior School, Faringdon

My Nan

My nan is very inquisitive like a cow
As funny as a monkey can be
As bald as a baby's bottom
As happy as a clown
As wobbly as a snake.
My nan is as wrinkly as a paper bag
As crazy as a kitten
As caring as a good nurse.

Kai Boyce (8)
Faringdon Junior School, Faringdon

What Is Blue?

Blue is a river, rippling and cool.
Blue is feeling upset and tears in a pool.
Blue is a bluebird swooping above,
Blue is when you're weeping, with no one to love.
Blue's a silent whisper drifting through the trees
Blue is the ice in the Arctic freeze.
Blue is the feeling you get when you've cried
Blue is the feeling when somebody's died.
Blue is the trickle that runs down your spine
When you're chilly and cold and the sun doesn't shine.

Rebecca Blundy (10)
Faringdon Junior School, Faringdon

My Grandad

My grandad is as funny as a clown although he is very old
When he goes out to work he gets there very cold
When I ask him for good advice he gives me what I want
My grandad is very tall, although he is very bald
He gives me things to hold
I love my grandad very much, although he is a nuisance
And he's very good at woodwork.

David Thomas (8)
Faringdon Junior School, Faringdon

What Is Black?

Black is a panther, prowling at night.
Black is feeling angry, scared with fright.
Black is a witch, casting a spell.
Sometimes black is going into a cell.
Black burns wildly in a bright fire
Black is a cauldron and the sound of a liar.
Black is the sadness you get inside
When you're upset and get put to the side.

Chloe Diamond (10)
Faringdon Junior School, Faringdon

The Extraordinary Dog

I am The Extraordinary Dog
I don't eat bones, dog food or meat
I crush and chew and mash and gobble:
               raspberry rulers
               blueberry pencils
               pineapple boards
I don't walk, sprint or train
I wobble like a duck and climb trees like a squirrel
I don't bark or beg
I laugh, I talk, I giggle and sing with the breeze
I am The Extraordinary Dog.

Katy Spiers (8)
Faringdon Junior School, Faringdon

The Extraordinary Dog

I am The Extraordinary Dog
I don't eat meat, dog food or bones
I chomp and chew and gulp and gobble:
               strawberry insects
               toffee and tomato wolves
               apple deer
I don't walk, run or jump
I hop and I fly like an aeroplane
I am The Extraordinary Dog.

Joe Hoskin (7)
Faringdon Junior School, Faringdon

The Extraordinary Dog

I am The Extraordinary Dog
I don't eat bones, meat or biscuits
I crunch, gulp and chomp:
       orange paper
       raspberry hair
       and mint rock
I don't run, swim or walk
I race, I pounce and I boogy
I don't bark, jump or sleep
I snort, laugh and smack
And I smell like hot chocolate
I am The Extraordinary Dog.

Ned Townsend (8)
Faringdon Junior School, Faringdon

The Extraordinary Dog

I don't eat meat, biscuits or lollies
I chomp and chew and gulp and gobble:
       chocolate crisps
       banana-flavoured pears
       mint flies.
I walk, hop and leap
I march, stomp and stamp
I don't play, bark or chase
I talk Japanese and I climb like monkeys
I am The Extraordinary Dog.

William James (7)
Faringdon Junior School, Faringdon

The Day They Played Football In My Garden

Treading up grass, my dad going crazy
Meg having the time of her life
Me playing
A rainy day in the backyard
Having a great time!
Getting soaked, Meg sliding on the tiles
Getting a cup of tea, stopping at half-time
Getting back into it. The ball going over the fence . . .
Oh great, so now we can't play!

Thomas O'Sullivan (9)
Faringdon Junior School, Faringdon

What Is Blue?

Blue is the sea, icy and cold
Blue is feeling sad and needing someone to hold.
Blue is the sky where birds fly and soar
Clouds float by and nothing's a chore.
Blue is a crystal, shiny and bright.
Blue is a parrot that sleeps at night.
Blue is coldness you get inside
When you cry and you want to hide.
Blue is a police siren going round and round
Blue is the colour I like and a brilliant sound.

Jack Sloan (8)
Faringdon Junior School, Faringdon

The Extraordinary Dog

I am The Extraordinary Dog
I don't eat meat, bones or cats
I chomp and chew and gulp and gobble . . .
     tomato unicorns
     toffee grass
     and ketchup curtains
I don't run, walk or jump
I flip and I gallop like a horse
I don't woof, bark or howl
I purr, zap and grumble
I am The Extraordinary Dog.

Sam Kenyon (7)
Faringdon Junior School, Faringdon

The Extraordinary Dog

I am The Extraordinary Dog
I don't eat bones, dog food or meat
I chomp and chew and gulp and gobble:
     mint rock rolls
     raspberry unicorns
     flavoured ham crisps
I don't jump, pounce or leap
I do headstands
I fly like a rocket and I howl
I am The Extraordinary Dog.

Eleanor Loasby (7)
Faringdon Junior School, Faringdon

The Extraordinary Dog

I am The Extraordinary Dog
I don't eat meat, bones or cats
I chomp and chew and gulp and gobble:
mint mice
chocolate cat food
cherry birds
I don't run, walk or jump
I hop, skip and I leap like a horse
I am The Extraordinary Dog.

Owen Foster (8)
Faringdon Junior School, Faringdon

Laughter Poem

Laughter is multicoloured like a firework bursting in your mouth.
It tastes like a crackling sweet in your mouth.
It smells like an apple pie steaming on the window ledge.
It looks like a big, round, orange pumpkin.
It feels like a warm, woolly rug.
It reminds me of the good, fun times me and my friends have.

Danielle Ruck (9)
Farnham Common Junior School, Farnham Common

Love Poem

Love is red or baby pink like peace.
It sounds like a bird singing on a summer day.
It tastes like ice cream.
It smells like Mum cooking my favourite dinner.
It looks like a new baby.
It feels like something going through my heart.
It reminds me of when I was a bridesmaid.

Hayley Marriott (8)
Farnham Common Junior School, Farnham Common

Sense Poem

Hunger is multicoloured like colours of a rainbow squirting out
It sounds like the bubbling of bubble bath
It tastes like you can't wait to eat
It smells like food is right in front of you
It looks like a pile of rocks
It feels like a volcano is rumbling inside your tummy
It reminds me of when I was starving on the way back from Wales.

Henry Gunn (8)
Farnham Common Junior School, Farnham Common

Silence

Silence is golden like the shiny sea,
It sounds like nothing,
It tastes like chocolate,
It smells like cake,
It looks like a hole of light,
It feels like something warm,
It reminds me of the empty playground.

Alice Crow (8)
Farnham Common Junior School, Farnham Common

Sense Poem

Hate is black like a dark cave
It sounds like some glass smashing
It tastes like some really hard metal
It smells like anger inside you
It looks like two sharks fighting together
It feels like you are going to burst
It reminds me of being kicked out of the football team.

Joel Wood (8)
Farnham Common Junior School, Farnham Common

Sense Poems

Fun is orange like playing in the playground
It sounds like children giggling
It tastes like chocolate
It smells like fresh air
It looks like fun
It feels like happiness
It reminds me of playing with my mum and dad.

Silence is like a golden apple
It sounds like me playing silently
It tastes like air
It smells like my favourite tea cooking
It looks like me reading a book in bed
It feels like lying in bed
It reminds me of work at school.

Emma Fryer (8)
Farnham Common Junior School, Farnham Common

Darkness

Darkness is black like a gloomy cellar,
It sounds like ghosts whistling through the air,
It tastes like air rushing in and out of my teeth,
It smells like a piece of bark,
It looks like a wall, very plain,
It feels like a squashy pear,
It reminds me of a black cat prowling through a tree.

Laughter is golden like the sunshine,
It sounds like fun racing from park to park,
It tastes like fruit flakes, creamy in my mouth,
It smells like the playground dust,
It looks like children having loads of fun,
It feels like a ball bouncy, bouncy, bong,
It reminds me of playing with a dog!

Madeleine Northwood (8)
Farnham Common Junior School, Farnham Common

Sense Poem

Darkness is black like there is no light at all
It sounds like there is no one about except you
It tastes like sour bread
It smells like ice cream, as cold as ice
It looks like everybody has gone and hidden
It feels like I am going to freeze
It reminds me of when my lights have gone off.

Fun is yellow like it's sunny and hot
It sounds like everybody is having fun
It smells like buttered toast
It tastes like sweets
It looks like flowers waiting to be picked
It feels like I am having the time of my life
It reminds me of when I am playing a fun game.

Hayley Marks (8)
Farnham Common Junior School, Farnham Common

Senses

Fun is multicoloured like a rainbow in the sky.
It sounds like children laughing and shouting.
It tastes sweet like sugar.
It smells like a chocolate factory.
It looks like a busy city.
It feels like a brilliant idea.
It reminds me of the bright sun.

Darkness is black like the middle of the night.
It sounds like an owl's call.
It tastes like a mouldy piece of cheese.
It looks like a blank piece of black card.
It feels like one hundred pins poking into you.
It reminds me of all the shadows.

Charlie Hewitt (9)
Farnham Common Junior School, Farnham Common

Sense Poem

Love is red like a chilli pepper on the grill
It sounds like the beating of a heart
It tastes like melted chocolate with ice cream
It smells like a warm chocolate milk shake
It looks like a shining heart
It feels like joy jumping in your tummy
It reminds me of my family.

Happiness is highlighted orange
Like a highlighted tiger of joy
It sounds like a hummingbird humming in the forest
It tastes like apple crumble
It smells like a pepperoni pizza
It looks like people having fun
It feels like stroking a dolphin.

Josh King (9)
Farnham Common Junior School, Farnham Common

Sense Poems

Love is pink like popcorn
It sounds like the sun setting
It tastes like sweets
It smells like flowers
It looks like hearts
It feels like wool
It reminds me of my family.

Sadness is blue like water
It sounds like falling leaves
It tastes like lemonade
It smells like smoke
It looks like a puddle
It feels like a petal
It reminds me of when I was sick.

Hannah Jeffery (8)
Farnham Common Junior School, Farnham Common

Sense Poems

Anger is red like a hot pepper
It sounds like fireworks
It tastes like fire in my mouth
It smells like burnt toast
It looks like a burning stove
It feels like burning soup
It reminds me of hot, burning anger.

Fun is green like grass
It sounds like grass swaying
It tastes like chocolate coming to you
It smells like fresh breeze in the sky
It feels like leaves
It reminds me of playing in the sky.

Ella Slais (8)
Farnham Common Junior School, Farnham Common

Sense Poems

Fear is like a black piece of paper
It sounds like a screaming woman
It tastes like mud
It smells like lava
It feels like a volcano exploding
It reminds me of a nightmare.

Sadness is like white
It sounds like crying
It tastes like onions
It smells like water
It looks like a big clock
It feels like chilli peppers.

Kristofor Stefan (8)
Farnham Common Junior School, Farnham Common

Sense Poem

Fun is multicoloured like a firework bursting in the air
It sounds like children chuckling and shouting
It tastes sweet like chocolate biscuits
It smells like a chocolate factory's chocolate
It looks like children running around the city
It feels like a cold fridge having a warm bath
It reminds me of winning a cup.

Silence is golden like the sunshine
It sounds like nothing
It tastes like you're not talking or doing anything
It smells like the grass swaying in the field
It feels like you're in space
It looks like nothing is in your mind
It reminds me of the quietest place in the world.

Laughter is silver like a spacesuit
It sounds like chattering monkeys
It smells like a fresh day
It looks like you have gone mad
It feels like you're going to die
It reminds me of friends.

Luke Hastings (8)
Farnham Common Junior School, Farnham Common

Love Poem

Love is red like lipstick
It smells like the sun rising at dawn
It tastes like the air settling in the evening
It sounds like the sea when you rattle a maraca
It looks like lipstick bright and lovely
It feels like a kiss on the move
It reminds me of a big, red rose.

Emma Hawkes (8)
Farnham Common Junior School, Farnham Common

Sense Poem

What colour is it?
Anger is red like a hot pepper
Anger sounds like a fire-breathing dragon
It tastes like a train screaming through the tunnel
It looks like a red-hot stove
It feels like a terrible dragon coming to get me
It reminds me of a hot bowl of soup

Fun is green like grass
It sounds like a really good feeling like the sun
It tastes like you have found a really good friend.

Katy Fletcher (8)
Farnham Common Junior School, Farnham Common

Sense Poem

Hate
Hate is grey like dark clouds
It sounds like two people fighting
It tastes like oil dripping from a car
It smells like dead people
It feels like someone's forgotten about me
It reminds me of people that are fighting.

Joseph Savage-Creighton (8)
Farnham Common Junior School, Farnham Common

Hate

Hate is like a volcano exploding, it is black.
It sounds like a boiler bubbling very hot.
It tastes like some really hard metal.
It smells like anger inside you.
It looks like two sharks fighting together.
It feels like you're going to burst.

Christopher Colliss (8)
Farnham Common Junior School, Farnham Common

Laughter

Laughter is blue like the ocean waves,
It tastes like salty water from the sea of life,
It sounds like joyful people playing on the beach,
It feels very funny and lovely like a clown in a circus,
It smells like rotten eggs and mushy peas mixed in a bowl,
It looks like a big pile of marshmallows,
It reminds me of my best friends.

William Hopwood (8)
Farnham Common Junior School, Farnham Common

Fun

Fun is blue like a sea on a lovely day,
Fun sounds like the wind blowing through the trees,
Fun tastes like chocolate in my mouth,
Fun reminds me of my mum,
Fun looks like a huge building of toys,
Fun smells like dinner when I come home,
Fun feels like someone tickling my back.

Matthew Jewson (8)
Farnham Common Junior School, Farnham Common

Happiness

Happiness is orange like a big brick
It looks like a kind old lady.
It tastes like a fresh apple.
It reminds me of my baby brother.
It smells like someone getting married.
It sounds like a cake being made.
It feels like a soft love poem.

George Quixley (8)
Farnham Common Junior School, Farnham Common

Happiness

Happiness is golden like the glistening sun in the air.
It feels like soft things all over my body.
Happiness smells like a clean nature world with lots of water.
It tastes like a fun McDonald's for all the family.
Happiness reminds me of my first goal for Beaconsfield SYCOB.
It looks like smiley faces everywhere in the world.
Happiness sounds like laughter in the house.

Alexander Tyler (8)
Farnham Common Junior School, Farnham Common

Hate

Hate is red like a burning flame.
It tastes like old, soggy fish in the sea.
It reminds me of strawberry jelly.
It smells like grey, horrible socks.
It looks like a red apple.
It feels like a big, sharp, thin knife.
It sounds like a bear fighting a hunter.

Ellie Meyer (8)
Farnham Common Junior School, Farnham Common

Love

Love is pink like the outdoors.
It reminds me of my dad.
It feels like the soft grass.
It looks like my heart.
It smells like poppies.
It tastes like a daffodil.
It sounds like the wind.

Luke Bentley (8)
Farnham Common Junior School, Farnham Common

Sadness

Sadness is blue like a shining sky.
It tastes like the sweetness of an apple, fresh from a tree.
It smells like the moon rising in the dark night.
It feels like chocolate melting in the sun when the day has just begun.
It sounds like my heart beating fast.
It looks like the yellow sun going down at the end of the day.
It reminds me of the places I've been to, like New Zealand.

Alexandra Taylor (8)
Farnham Common Junior School, Farnham Common

Silence

Silence is white like a brand new start.
It smells like apple pie fresh from the oven.
It sounds like the wind blowing through the trees.
It feels like a soft cushion lying on my sofa.
It tastes like blueberries resting in my tummy.
It looks like the sun, blazing hot in the sky.
It reminds me of the waves crashing on the shore.

Harry Dymond (9)
Farnham Common Junior School, Farnham Common

Anger

Anger is red, like blood dripping from a vampire's fangs.
It tastes like red-hot chilli peppers.
It feels like a really rough stone.
It smells like a spicy curry.
It reminds me of the sound of shouting.
It looks like a shark snapping away.

James Llewelyn (8)
Farnham Common Junior School, Farnham Common

Silence

Silence is black like burnt lava.
Silence smells like smoke coming out from a chimney.
Silence feels like dust floating past your face.
Silence reminds me of the cars driving past during the day.
Silence looks like a person thinking about what he is going
                                    to be when he is older.
Silence sounds like life passing through time.
Silence tastes like seawater from the ocean.

Matty Paine (8)
Farnham Common Junior School, Farnham Common

Sadness

Sadness is turquoise like rain dropping from the morning sky.
It feels like the shivering of the snowman melting as the sun
                                    comes up at dawn.
It smells like a summer's day when the flowers start to droop.
It sounds like the dripping of the tap as I wash my wrinkled hands.
It tastes like the juice from an apple spreading round my tongue.
It looks like the amber leaves that rustle and tumble around.
It reminds me of all the times I've heard my new puppy whimper.

Olivia Jennings (8)
Farnham Common Junior School, Farnham Common

Fear

Fear is green like grass in a graveyard.
It feels like a red-hot flame of fire.
It smells like tyre wheels from a jeep.
It reminds me of my mean brother.
It looks like a swimming pool full of sharks.
It sounds like a black bull with long white horns.

Alex Parkinson (8)
Farnham Common Junior School, Farnham Common

Laughter

Laughter is *pink* like tasty strawberry ice cream.
Laughter tastes like pure pink cotton candy falling from the sky.
Laughter looks like thousands of pounds floating in the sky.
Laughter smells like fresh baguettes that have just come
out of the oven.
Laughter sounds like billions of people cheering for England
to win the football match and they do.
Laughter feels like Jesus putting His love into your heart.
Laughter reminds me of the happiness of the whole world.

Kristie Killick (8)
Farnham Common Junior School, Farnham Common

Laughter

Laughter is silver like the Queen's jewels,
It tastes like happiness playing with your friends,
It sounds like a playground full with playful children,
It looks like trees blowing in the distance,
It smells like flowers that make you sneeze,
It feels like nothing could be better,
It reminds me of Christmas when everyone's happy.

Simran Jhooty (8)
Farnham Common Junior School, Farnham Common

Happiness

Happiness is blue like the sparkling sea,
Happiness tastes like chocolate from a chocolate factory,
Happiness smells like air freshener,
Happiness looks like Chelsea winning against Arsenal,
Happiness sounds like a big cheer,
Happiness feels like I have won the lottery,
Happiness reminds me of my baby cousin being born.

Holly Holmes (8)
Farnham Common Junior School, Farnham Common

Fear

It is the colour of dark purple like a blackberry getting
                                           ready be picked.
It smells like a fire burning on my skin.
It feels like a rose dying for water.
It looks like a cold bird moaning for food.
It sounds like a person crying because they have fallen over.
It tastes like the rough sea, *swish, swish,* as it goes.
It reminds me of my puppy whimpering when I'm gone.

Natasha Torpy (9)
Farnham Common Junior School, Farnham Common

Fear

Fear is the colour of pale pink.
It sounds like you are very scared.
It reminds me of crying.
It tastes like water about to explode in your mouth.
It smells like strawberry-flavoured water.
It looks like a pink drawing on your cheek.
It feels like water about to spring from your eyes.

Harry Fernberg (8)
Farnham Common Junior School, Farnham Common

The Poem Of Laughter

Laughter is light red like candy.
It tastes like sweets and chocolates.
It looks like a red face that is grinning.
The smell is like ice cream and all the things you like.
It feels really, really happy.
It sounds like strange giggles.
It reminds me of going to Thorpe Park with Holly.

Alice Simmonds (8)
Farnham Common Junior School, Farnham Common

Anger

Anger is maroon like a drop of blood
It sounds like a hungry, grizzly bear roaring
It looks like a fire-breathing dragon
It smells like a year-old piece of dog food
It feels like a piece of gunk
It tastes like rotten eggs
It feels like burning hot tea on your tongue
It reminds me of a volcano.

Harry Ray (8)
Farnham Common Junior School, Farnham Common

Darkness

Darkness is like the colour black.
It smells like lovely fresh seafood.
It feels like something really weird.
It tastes quite strange.
It sounds like the wind.
The darkness reminds me of the night
And makes me feel tired and want to go to bed.

Darcey Yost (8)
Farnham Common Junior School, Farnham Common

Darkness

Darkness is the darkest black.
Darkness is like a hollow cave at night.
It sounds like the dripping of an icicle.
It looks like a man in disguise.
It tastes like a rotten egg.
It reminds me of the scariest scare.
The smell of danger is in the air.

Alex Bristow (8)
Farnham Common Junior School, Farnham Common

Hate

Hate is red like fresh blood from a wound.
Hate feels like red-hot lava trickling down your skin.
Hate tastes like two-week-old rotten eggs.
Hate sounds like an angry volcano about to erupt.
Hate smells like mouldy cheese.
Hate looks like a red demon with a flaming fork.
Hate reminds me of a great white shark looking for its prey.

Peter Adigun (9)
Farnham Common Junior School, Farnham Common

Sadness

Sadness is blue like the sky,
It smells like a cold winter's morning,
It looks like deep sorrow,
It feels like the most upsetting thing,
It sounds like people crying a lot,
It tastes like cold ice,
It reminds me of a baby screaming.

Rosie Light (8)
Farnham Common Junior School, Farnham Common

Winter

D ogs are playing in the snow.
E very day freezing snow falls.
C old ice freezes ponds and rivers.
E verybody goes sledging.
M y hands go purple as the wind blows.
B abies have been put next to the fire to keep warm.
E xcited children throwing snowballs.
R unning about making snowmen.

Fern Davis (8)
Glory Farm CP School, Bicester

Oliver

Down in the workhouse,
The monstrous, prison warehouse,
There is
Starvation.
The tired boy works
On the cold, stone floor,
And all are
Skin and bone.

Up in the attic,
The dark, dingy attic,
There is
Food!
The hungry boy stares
At the warm, filling cooking,
And all is
Sleepy.

Down in the house,
The warm, welcoming house,
There is
Kindness.
The happy boy sleeps
In the soft, comfortable bed,
And all is
Peaceful.

Megan Kunzer (11)
Glory Farm CP School, Bicester

Winter

Chilly people round the toasty fire,
Old leaves half-buried in the snow,
Little angels making snow angels.
Dreams are of Christmas Day.

Ellie Andrews (8)
Glory Farm CP School, Bicester

Oliver

Down in the workhouse,
The dusty, filthy workhouse,
There is
Mayhem!
The guilty master smells
In the huge, tatty workhouse
And all are starving.

Up in the attic,
The deep, dark attic
There are
Sausages!
The mischievous Dodger sleeps
In the smelly, gloomy room
And all is stolen.

Up in the bedroom,
The high-class bedroom
There is
Oliver!
The sly snitch awaits
In the gruesome, slimy alley
And all is
Evil.

Arlo Union (10)
Glory Farm CP School, Bicester

Oliver

Up in the attic,
The dark, dusty attic,
There is
Smoke!

The slick man counts
In the cold, smelly attic
And all is
Silent.

Anthony Jaggs (10)
Glory Farm CP School, Bicester

Oliver

Down in the streets
The dark, gloomy streets,
There is
Darkness.

The sneaky thieves sleep
In the black, scary attic
And all is
Grim!

Up in the attic,
The black, dark attic
There are
Boys.

The ragged boys sleep
in the tatty smelly beds
And all is
Dirty!

Ben Blatcher (10)
Glory Farm CP School, Bicester

Oliver Twist

Down in the workhouse,
The grimy, horrible workhouse
There is
Starvation!

The plump headmaster eats
And the poor orphans work
And all is
Miserable!

The poor forcibly scrounge
So the filthy rich enjoy
And all is
Uneven.

Steven Davidson (10)
Glory Farm CP School, Bicester

Oliver Twist

Round in the orphanage
The dirty, tatty orphanage
There is
Starvation.

The shabby, ragged children
Sleep in the dirty, smelly beds
And all is
Silent.

Out in the streets
The filthy, shabby streets
There is
Tiredness.

The desperate people sleep
In the poor, tatty streets
And all is
Dark.

Siobhan Chicken (11)
Glory Farm CP School, Bicester

Oliver Twist

Down in the workhouse,
The shadowy, icy workhouse
There is malnutrition.
The voracious orphan sleeps
On the prostrate, wooden planks,
And all is
Mute.

Down in the street,
The reeking, dusty street
There is haze
The tiny boy roams
Through the long, gloomy alley
And all is
Booming.

Michael Northcott 10)
Glory Farm CP School, Bicester

Difference Poem

Round in the orphanage,
The shabby, tatty orphanage
There is
Hunger.

The filthy boy works
While the fat master eats
And all is
Rumbling.

Down in the streets,
The dusty, filthy streets
There is
Mischief.

The shabby boy steals
While the exhausted people cry
And all is
Silent.

Up in the room,
The splendid silver room
There is
Glitter.

The gentle man sleeps
While the orphans work
And all is
Pleasant.

Shannon Bardwell (10)
Glory Farm CP School, Bicester

Winter

Chilly air is all around.
Old and torn leaves fall to the ground.
Lovely cold, cold ice filling every pond.
'Daddy, wake up, Christmas Day has come.'

Bethany Smith (8)
Glory Farm CP School, Bicester

Switching

Down on the streets,
The scary, gloomy streets
There is
Despair.

The pickpockets steal
While the fading shadows glow
And all is
Silent.

Up in the room,
The spotless, golden room
There is
Sunlight.

The maid comes in
While the little boy sleeps
And all are
Woken.

Rachel Walden (10)
Glory Farm CP School, Bicester

Summer

I'm hot, steaming
like a teapot
it's so hot I'm melting
like a chocolate drop
    melt
        melt
oh, I wish I could have
a drink of pop fizz
fizz cool
cool, can I give the baby
in the cot a bit of pop?

Molly Lyons (7)
Glory Farm CP School, Bicester

My Gran

My gran is as crinkly as a bag.
My gran's hair is as pink as candyfloss.
Her eyes are as brown as mud.
Her face is like a pink, old sausage.
When she walks she's like a kangaroo.
When she sits she is like the laziest person in the world.
When she coughs she sounds like a witch when she has
                                        made a magic potion.

Grace Julier (8)
Glory Farm CP School, Bicester

Summer Spell

This is my summer place
And all the leaves are as long as palm leaves
And the river is as slow as a snail.
The weather is as hot as a barbecue.
The air is as breezy as the Caribbean.
My voice is as loud as a speaker
And everything is like an inferno.

Liam Duggan (8)
Glory Farm CP School, Bicester

Winter

W hite snow as bright as the sun
 I s fun and cold
N ever boring.
T o make a snowball is easy
E veryone can play.
R ough in your hands.

Jamie Wilson (8)
Glory Farm CP School, Bicester

Children's Day Out

A bus is waiting at my school,
We are going to the swimming pool,
I sit in the bus all nice and cool,
I bet it will be hot in the pool.

My bus driver is tall and thin.
He also has a double chin.
We're here at last,
I wonder how the time will pass?

I'm in the pool with all my friends,
I hope that this will never end.

Chloe Lewitt (7)
Glory Farm CP School, Bicester

Water Monster

Down in the deep pool
with all my friends,
every time I thought
there was a water monster.
And then I was sunk by
the big, water monster.
I was so afraid
because I might die.

Liam John Barnes (7)
Glory Farm CP School, Bicester

Ice

Ice is cold.
Ice is slippery.
Before it melts
It looks very pretty.

Poppy Cooper (7)
Glory Farm CP School, Bicester

Home

Listen!
(What can you hear?)
Listen!
(What can you hear?)
The squeak of a guinea pig
Listen!
(What can you hear?)
A bang of a book.
Listen!
(What can you hear?)
Baby screaming.

Harry Card (7)
Glory Farm CP School, Bicester

How To Get Out Of Detention

First of all you stare the teacher in the eye
until their eyes are watering,
after that you put a pair of unwashed gym socks in a cup,
with a few toenail clippings.
Stir with a ruler and add some cold tea,
that the teacher brought a week ago.
Leave for a night
then put a sprinkle of water on top
and the teacher will forget everything they said.

> *I will never flick paper at the teacher,*
> *I will never flick paper at the teacher,*
> *I will never flick paper at the teacher,*
> *I will never flick paper at the teacher,*
> *I will never flick paper at the teacher,*
> *I will never . . .*

Alec Newton (10)
Hawkhurst Primary School, Hawkhurst

Blue Seasons

Blue summer
On holiday you go in the sea.
The sea is blue and we swim in it,
Underwater and up again.
Your brother jumps on you, he's a pain.

Blue winter
All your friends get their skates.
Blue as water, you skate on the ice.
The ice is blue water but gets frozen up.
Wow! This is fun, I'll do it again tomorrow.

Blue spring
Blue spring is all around us.
Blue flowers are springing up in flowerbeds.
Newborn baby dolphins swim in the oceans.
Blue spring is everywhere.

Blue autumn
The sky is blue in autumn.
The blue tits fly in the sky in autumn.
They peck the nuts from the net in autumn.

Blue seasons are all through the year.

Rowan Thomas (10)
Hawkhurst Primary School, Hawkhurst

The Green Seaside

The sound of the waves as they crash together.
The smell of rotten fish.
The taste of lovely spinach.
The weather is raining.
The feel of sloppy seaweed between my feet.
The joy of the green in the rainbow.
My favourite jewel is jade from down in the sea
From a treasure chest.

Megan Smith (8)
Hawkhurst Primary School, Hawkhurst

My Wildest Wish To Have A Pet Werewolf

Firs you need a wolf's head,
then you need a dead man's legs,
a hog's eye,
a bear's fur coat,
a newt's skin fresh from the bin,
a stick of glue.
Rub it all over them
put them in the freezer for a minute or two.
There's a pet werewolf just for you!

Jake Barnes (9)
Hawkhurst Primary School, Hawkhurst

My Spell For My Wildest Wish

I want a pig please.
I want a pig that snores please.
I want a pig that plays in the mud and snorts please,
and plays *bingo* please.
I want a pig that snorts, plays in the mud
and plays bingo and flies please.
I want a pig.

Kieran Jones (9)
Hawkhurst Primary School, Hawkhurst

Green Is The Colour

The joy of Miss Dixon's favourite chair.
The joy of the common seal swimming by.
The joy of lily pads that common frogs can sit on.
The happy Easter cotton rabbits go hopping by.
Hearing the sound of whales weaving by.

Victoria Clayson (8)
Hawkhurst Primary School, Hawkhurst

How To Get A Flying Pig

First get some bacon
then get some sausages
and put them in a pot
then some mud.
Add two feathers
and some icing
and put all of that
in and a flying pig
will come out.

Dominic Bishop (7)
Hawkhurst Primary School, Hawkhurst

The 'At' Cat

There was a fat cat
who chased a rat.
He slept on a mat
and wore a black hat.
He liked to play bat
with his friend called Pat.

Henry Sculley, Vincent King,
**   Michael Gardiner & Phillip Brown (9)**
Hawkhurst Primary School, Hawkhurst

My World Of Nature

My grass is blue, I've got the flu
        Rabbits are pink, well, I think
Horses are yellow, all skinny and mellow
        Dogs are white, cats, light
Foxes are extinct, badgers stink
        My world is the best
There is no theft
        'Cause my world is just the best.

Rachael Lloyd (9)
Hawkhurst Primary School, Hawkhurst

A Spell To Change Your Life Forever - Make Yourself Into A Sports Star

Ingredients
Find a cauldron,
Collect up:
Kelly Holmes' trainers
(The ones she wore ten years ago,
she'll have grown out of them now)
Jonny Wilkinson's rugby shirt,
Wayne Rooney's shin pads,
and David James' goalie gloves.

Method
Put fourteen litres of freezing cold water
into the cauldron and stand it over the fire
for two hours and wait for it to boil,
add the above ingredients and stir vigorously.

Melt down four Olympic gold medals
with the World Cup until extremely runny.

Strain the juice from the sports stars' clothes
and whisk into the molten metal.
Allow to cool slightly before serving in a cocktail glass.
Drink while chanting, 'We are the Champions' in Latin.

Serving suggestion:
Add two cloves of garlic to fend off your competitors
and three sugar lumps for added energy.

Charlotte Robinson (9)
Hawkhurst Primary School, Hawkhurst

Green

The taste of . . . juicy Granny Smith apples.
The sound of . . . fresh grass.
The feel of . . . chairs, all bumpy
The smell of . . . a spring morning
The joy of . . . a comfy chair.

Emily Morris (8)
Hawkhurst Primary School, Hawkhurst

The Shadow Lion

When I see a shadow
I don't know what it is
Maybe a tiger or a lion
Or maybe a ghost?

But I just saw a shadow
Under the tree
It was moving towards me
But then I saw a light and I was free.

I walked towards the light
But it wasn't the light
It was the shadow lion
But it couldn't be true!

But it was the shadow lion,
He had sharp claws, beady eyes,
Vampire teeth, long sharp tail,
And shadow powers.

Then suddenly the shadow lion was gone!
But where did he go?

Ryan Huggins (9)
Hawkhurst Primary School, Hawkhurst

Green

The precious jewel, emerald, glistening in the sunshine,
The leaves in the summer on a chestnut or pine tree,
The smell of the vegetables in the garden, gradually growing,
The joy of playing on the grassy fields,
The hopping frogs bouncing from lily pad to lily pad,
The delicious taste of Granny Smith apples that grow on trees,
The best thing my friend likes to eat is peas, peas, peas,
The field of meadowy grass from the view of a flight,
The precious jewel, jade, shines in the moonlight.

Chloe-Mae Thorpe (8)
Hawkhurst Primary School, Hawkhurst

A Spell To Make All Parents Do What You Want

First choose a parent.
Collect their least favourite food,
And plenty of washing up liquid
(To wash away all ideas of a healthy tea!)

Pour the liquid over the food,
Put the mixture in a saucepan,
(Watch out, Dad's coming in!)
Boil for ten minutes.

Place saucepan in a cupboard,
Wait for Mum and Dad,
And yell, 'Washing up liquid, do your best.
Stop my parents being a pest!'
(And if it doesn't work, don't blame me).

Chloë de Lullington (9)
Hawkhurst Primary School, Hawkhurst

Green

The smell of cucumber sandwiches.
The smell of the sea.
A sunny day in the summer.
Someone tickling your toes.
The taste of yoghurt.
Smelling the leaves on a spring morning.
Telling a poem about people.
Drawing a picture.
When I win a game.
When I meet my friend.
When I go bike riding.
When I go to school.
When I get my hair cut.

Leanne Ellis (8)
Hawkhurst Primary School, Hawkhurst

The Spell: How To Get A Puppy

Ingredients:
First you need to have:
Two frogs' legs,
one cat's ear,
two wasp stings
some dog food.

Method:
First you must have a pot and put in the two wasp stings.
The you must add the two frogs' legs and the dog food.
Then stir it for five minutes.
Then put it into the fridge and wait till morning.
In the morning, go downstairs and open the fridge
and there should be a puppy.

Katie Thirkell (9)
Hawkhurst Primary School, Hawkhurst

How To Be A Pop Star

Ingredients:
Four petals off a rose.
A sprinkle of sugar.
A pinch of luck.
A strand of hair.
A CD of your favourite pop star.
Some of your make-up.
Clean water.
Glitter.
A bottle of perfume
Your favourite colour
And a magazine

Method:
Put ingredients into a cup and drink.

Rebecca Palmer (9)
Hawkhurst Primary School, Hawkhurst

Green

The sound of an albatross going over the beach in the mist.
The smell of spinach being cooked, it makes you strong.
The taste of jelly wobbling.
The feel of crabs pinching my feet.
The joy of swimming with dolphins.
The luxury of having a Jacuzzi.
The crunch of fresh cabbage from the fridge.
The healthy leaves on the palm tree.
The movements of snakes that slither and slide.

Harvey Daniel (8)
Hawkhurst Primary School, Hawkhurst

Green Field

Sound of tractors cutting the grass,
Smell of flowers just about to bloom.
The taste of toast in the morning,
It's a really sunny day,
The sun is really shining on my relaxed vertebrae.

Thomas Parrish (9)
Hawkhurst Primary School, Hawkhurst

Green

The freshly cut grass in the summer,
The sound of a peaceful spring morning,
The feel of the seaweed in-between your bare toes,
The pleasure of playing football with my brother,
The smell of the sea crashing against the cliffs.

Robyn Matthews (9)
Hawkhurst Primary School, Hawkhurst

Green

The sound of grass being cut after the rain,
The stormy weather bouncing off the windowpane.
The taste of cucumber freshly bought,
The feel of a fresh leaf that I just caught.
The smell of marrow that Dad's just dug up,
The joy of sunbathing with my new pup!
The sun has come up, I'm going out again,
I'm going to the park that is just down the lane.

Ben Smith (9)
Hawkhurst Primary School, Hawkhurst

Green

The smell of grass when it is freshly cut.
The sound of birds rustling in and out of trees.
The taste of Granny Smith, Braeburn and Cox's apples.
The splash of rain as it bounces on my window.
The feel of my soft teddy when I cuddle it on a summer morning.
The joy of seeing baby animals in the spring.

Charlotte Louise Gould (8)
Hawkhurst Primary School, Hawkhurst

Green

The sound of a cuckoo in the woods
The taste of an apple, juicy
The feeling of being happy
The shape of green, bright leaves
The sound of the branches breaking.

Tyler Davies & Louis Breck (8)
Hawkhurst Primary School, Hawkhurst

Love

It sounds like a heart beating very, very slowly,
It looks like doves flying in the sky at midnight,
It smells like lovely, beautiful and smelly perfume,
It reminds me of my mummy and daddy getting married in church.
It feels like people on their first date in a restaurant,
It is pink like two people kissing at sunset on the beach
                                on the soft sand.

Sarah Palmer (7)
Hawkhurst Primary School, Hawkhurst

Green

I like the taste of juicy apples.
I like the feel of seaweed in-between my toes
I like the smell of pears.
I like the sound of leaves blowing back and forth
On a summer's day.
I like the joy of cosy chairs.

Samantha Merrett (8)
Hawkhurst Primary School, Hawkhurst

Green

The smell of the fresh sea
Feeling the seaweed between my fingers
The taste of Granny Smith apples
The joy of a comfy chair
The sound of the crashing waves.

Lauren Kerr (8)
Hawkhurst Primary School, Hawkhurst

Love

It reminds me of pink and red beautiful flowers in the
                                                    Queen's garden,
It feels like soft white cats just born in a church,
It sounds like beautiful birds singing in the blossom tree,
It is light pink like a butterfly in a box,
It looks like red hearts floating in a heaven of white clouds,
It smells like blue roses picked freshly from the garden.

Robyn Eldred (7)
Hawkhurst Primary School, Hawkhurst

Green

The colour of my face when I'm on a boat.
The healthy leaves of a sunflower.
The taste of a juicy kiwi.
The crunch of fresh celery.
A rabbit eating the leaves of a carrot.
The smell of grass on a rugby field.

Rosie Wood (8)
Hawkhurst Primary School, Hawkhurst

Green

The sound of the scraping of a pen.
The smell of freshly cut grass
The feel of lovely, soft cushions in a hot room.
The joy of jumping into a warm, peaceful swimming pool.

Jacob Collins (9)
Hawkhurst Primary School, Hawkhurst

Green

The sound of birds when they sing their chirpy song.
The smell of lettuce in the middle of the table.
The look of parrots when you see their tails.
The taste of lovely ice cream.
The joy of sunbathing in the sun.
The sound of birds when they sing their chirpy song.

Ainsley Weston (8)
Hawkhurst Primary School, Hawkhurst

Green Is The Colour

The sound of a greenfinch flying in the gentle breeze.
The smell of grass when it has been freshly cut.
The taste of apple pie just after it has been cooked.
An evening near the sea just as it turns to dusk.
The feel of when I'm doing a puzzle.
The joy of watching a seal next to the water.

Ryan Baker (9)
Hawkhurst Primary School, Hawkhurst

What Is Green?

The sound of the sea splashing
The smell of fresh grapes
The taste of juicy apples
The joy of comfy chairs with cushions
The feel of jade and emerald.

Bethan Eastwood (8)
Hawkhurst Primary School, Hawkhurst

Love

It looks like happiness meeting in the fresh air,
It smells like fresh clean air flowing into your heart,
It reminds me of my caring, loving, happy family,
It feels like you're meeting a new heart and person for love,
It sounds like your heart is beating very fast, ready for love,
It is like love meeting you in the air and making you happy.

Holly Wetherell (7)
Hawkhurst Primary School, Hawkhurst

Hate

It feels like you don't want to be their friend anymore,
It is red like a blasting volcano,
It reminds me of a bully bullying me,
It sounds like anger and someone getting cross,
It looks like someone is getting cross and going red,
It smells like burning hot smoke spreading around the village.

Emily Wetherell (7)
Hawkhurst Primary School, Hawkhurst

Green

The grass is green that shines through the moonlight
The trees are green with shiny leaves on them
Pears are green with lots of taste in them
Jade is green, it twinkles in the moonlight
We are in a green class, where we get taught.

Charlotte Clayson (8)
Hawkhurst Primary School, Hawkhurst

Green

The sound of a frog sitting on a petal,
The smell of freshly cut grass on an early morning,
The taste of the inside of a kiwi,
The joy of sitting on my grandad's lovely armchair,
The feel of slimy seaweed between my toes.

Henry Bruce (8)
Hawkhurst Primary School, Hawkhurst

Green!

The taste of the spring fresh air.
The sound of the wonderful crickets splashing in the grass.
The joy of the autumn grasshoppers hopping around the meadow.
The sunshine glittering in the sky.

James Cox (8)
Hawkhurst Primary School, Hawkhurst

Green!

The feeling of seaweed around my toes.
The feeling of jelly up my nose.
A frog bouncing around my toes.
Green! Is the colour that goes with those.

Max Wood (8)
Hawkhurst Primary School, Hawkhurst

Happiness

It smells like beautiful flowers.
It feels like stroking a cuddly pet.
It looks like a shining bright sun.
It is blue like the blue sea.
It reminds me of the animals in a wild wood.

Adam MacKelden (7)
Hawkhurst Primary School, Hawkhurst

Football Crazy

Football fever
Football fever
Let's all watch the football diva.
Every team trying to score
But the goalie's like a wooden door.
Managers shouting
Managers doubting
Will they score?
Will they score?
Football fans drink out of cans,
Out of cans
Football fever
Football fever
Let's all watch the football diva!

Sebastian Renshaw (9)
Headcorn CP School, Ashford

The Moon Glows

The moon shimmers
Like a treasure chest under my bed.

The moon glows
Like a shiny star from outer space.

The moon twinkles
Like a shining, beautiful locket around your neck.

The moon reflects
Like a box of jewels in a police cell.

The moon dazzles
Like a silver coin in someone's purse.

Danielle Groves (9)
Headcorn CP School, Ashford

The Moon

The moon shines
Like a scaly fish in the deep sea.

The moon glows
Like a firefly.

The moon glistens
Like polished shoes in the porch.

The moon sparkles
Like a star in the sky.

The moon shimmers
Like the mirror in a bathroom.

Gregory Harris (9)
Headcorn CP School, Ashford

The Moon

The moon glows
Like a lantern in the porch

The moon dazzles
Like a fading candle in the lighthouse

The moon twinkles
Like a thousand stars in the sky

The moon reflects
Like a lit pumpkin outside my back door

The moon blazes
Like a night float in the pond.

Christopher Gorman (9)
Headcorn CP School, Ashford

The Moon

The moon gleams
Like a reflection in the pond.

The moon glistens
Like a lemon sherbet on the window sill.

The moon glows
Like a jacket zip on the tie rack.

The moon illuminates
Like a globe in a child's bedroom.

The moon sparkles
Like a glittery gel pen in its opened case.

Alexander Warren (9)
Headcorn CP School, Ashford

The Moon

The moon glows
Like a fading sparkler on Bonfire Night.

The moon glimmers
Like a diamond necklace in a jewellery shop window.

The moon glistens
Like a bright star in the night sky.

The moon shimmers
Like a reflection of itself in the water.

The moon sparkles
Like a silver penny at the bottom of a pond.

Chloe Wilson (9)
Headcorn CP School, Ashford

I Close My Eyes

I close my eyes and I see
kittens being loved and cared for.
I close my eyes and I see
pretty patterns swirling around me.
I close my eyes and I see
twinkling fairies fluttering in-between
the moon and the stars.
I close my eyes and I see
the beautiful countryside.
I open my eyes and I see
the ones I love.

Sarah Chattell (7)
Headcorn CP School, Ashford

I Close My Eyes

I close my eyes and I see
a diamond tree twinkling brightly in the stars.
I close my eyes and I see
a big, hairy monster chasing me round a light.
I close my eyes and I see
a gigantic rainbow with lights flashing brightly.
I open my eyes and I see
the extraordinary world around me.

Ella Buckle (8)
Headcorn CP School, Ashford

When I Watch Golf

When I watch golf I watch Tiger Woods putting the ball halfway
down the fairway into a bunker.
When I watch golf I watch Clarke beating Ben Hogan.
When I watch golf I watch Europe winning the Ryder Cup.
When I watch golf I watch my dad hitting another tree.
When I watch golf I watch my grandad getting a hole in one.

Jack Morgan (8)
Headcorn CP School, Ashford

The Moon

The moon glows
Like a milky pearl from a fresh oyster.
The moon twinkles
Like a sparkling disco ball at a party.
The moon shines
Like a fading torch in a forest at night.
The moon glints
Like a lemon sliced in half.
The moon reflects
Like a river with the moonlight.

Josie Sharp (9)
Headcorn CP School, Ashford

The Moon

The moon shimmers
Like a night float in the gloomy pond.

The moon glistens
Like a fading torch in the dark forest

The moon glows
Like a reflection in a pond

The moon glows
Like a lantern lit in a library.

Tom Necci (9)
Headcorn CP School, Ashford

The Wind In The Trees

When I hear the wind in the trees,
I think of the four seasons,
The fresh air in spring,
And the summer's cool breezes,
So listen to the sounds of nature,
And think of your favourite things.

Grace Dickins (7)
Headcorn CP School, Ashford

I See A Star

I see a star
twinkling

I see a star
shining

I see a star
brighter and brighter

I see a star
blaze with all its power

I see a star
disappear.

Jim Owen (8)
Headcorn CP School, Ashford

I Close My Eyes And I See

I close my eyes and I see
starlight.
I close my eyes and I see
pretty shapes everywhere.
I close my eyes and I see
a fairy looking at me.
I close my eyes and I see
a crystal rainbow.
I open my eyes and I see
the wide world.

Jessica Moseley (8)
Headcorn CP School, Ashford

The Night-Time

Owls hooting softly,
Mice scurrying across the lonely field,
Wind whistling gently through the dark sky,
Bats flapping their furry wings,
Foxes sniff the cool air,
Hedgehogs snuffle around,
Cats scratch at the fence.

As the night turns into day,
Owls sleep in their beds,
Mice lie in their dens,
The wind softens,
And bats hang upside down on branches,
Foxes sleep in their lairs,
Hedgehogs lie in their holes,
Cats go back inside,
Children come out to play,
Another start to a wonderful day.

Abigail Foster (8)
Kings Court School, Old Windsor

The Moon

The wind is whistling in the full moon
Hailstones clattering on car rooftops
Everyone sleeps in silence
Moon shines in my window
Over the hill the wind howls
Over in the corner cats gather
Nearby the bay, boats sway.

Matthew Brewis (9)
Kings Court School, Old Windsor

Sounds

I can hear bears howling
in the distance.
I can see trees swaying
in the windy weather.
I can feel sad and worried as I walk
among the towering trees above me.
I can hear the wind whistling
in and out of the trees.
I can see birds cleaning
their feathers in the trees.
I can feel the stones
inside my shoes.

Ellie Welch (8)
Kings Court School, Old Windsor

The Moon

The moon is twinkling in the night.
Hedgehogs are plodding across the grass.
Everybody is sleeping while the foxes are hunting.
Morning is dawning and the moon is dying.
Outside the boats are swaying.
Octopuses are hidden under the rocks.
Now the night has gone and the sun comes up.

George Fowler (8)
Kings Court School, Old Windsor

The Moon

Cats purring in the dark.
Bats out looking for food, swaying and swooping
in and out of the trees.
Hedgehogs snuffling through the leaves.
A doorbell rings but nobody answers it!

Aaron Stephenson (8)
Kings Court School, Old Windsor

The Moon

The whistling wind waits and waits till dawn breaks.
The sun goes down, the moon comes up.
Dogs howling for a new day to come
And the moon is the only light we'll see.
The dawn comes then fades away.
The chilly wind swoops from house to house.
Misty fog covers the road.
People shivering in their beds.

Helena Clisby (9)
Kings Court School, Old Windsor

The Moon

In space black holes are eating.
Cats are fighting in the bin.
Shadows on the road.
Dogs barking, cats miaowing.
Wolves howling.
Bats screeching.
Bears growling.
All happening in the night.

Ryan Whearty (8)
Kings Court School, Old Windsor

Outside At Night

Owls hooting, werewolves howling.
Bats screeching and cats miaowing.
Foxes prowling, hedgehogs running.
Rats squeaking and dogs barking.
Children sleeping, spiders creeping.
Tapes recording, apples falling.
Doors creaking, windows slamming.
Wind rustles leaves on the ground.

Oliver Wood (8)
Kings Court School, Old Windsor

My Noisy Forest Poem

I can hear the birds singing in the darkness.
I can hear the wolves howling behind me.
I can hear the trees rustling all around me.
I can see the birds cleaning their feathers in the puddles.
I can see creatures getting closer and frightening me.
I can hear the owl tooting in the treetops.
I can hear the squirrels jumping from tree to tree.
I feel like I don't want to go home.
I can see the flowers waving in the mud.

Danni Short (7)
Kings Court School, Old Windsor

The Stars

The stars are out.
The sky is all bright and shining.
So bright that I can even see myself in it.
I wish I could go up there just once
Then come back down again.
All sparkly glittery.
It looks like a diamond ring.
If I could only wear it!
Stars are twinkling.

Amber Waheed (8)
Kings Court School, Old Windsor

The Moon

The moon is shining brightly.
Hailstones stamping on the ground.
Everybody snuggled up in their beds.
Mice squeaking all over the place.
Bats hanging on trees upside down.
Spiky hedgehogs hunting for food.
Now morning has come and children play.

Suhaib Riaz (9)
Kings Court School, Old Windsor

The Dark Night

The wind whistles through the dark sky
Wolves howl in the woods
Hedgehogs snuffle
Floorboards creak through the silent house
Foxes run through the bushes
The moon shines down on the sleeping children
Curtains flap through the open window
The lonely cat lies on the wall
Looking at the mice scurrying across the road.

Lizzie Fielder (8)
Kings Court School, Old Windsor

A Forest Poem

I am walking in the dark gloomy forest.
I can hear crickets and birds calling.
It's getting much darker.
I can see towering trees surrounding me.
I can hear leaves crunching as I tread on them.
I can see deer in the distance.
I can hear creatures running through the bushes.
I can hear wind in a little breeze.

Brandon Reilly (7)
Kings Court School, Old Windsor

The Dark Night

In the misty night, where the wind is whistling,
Owls are hooting.
Everyone is asleep.
Children are dreaming about the man in the moon.
Bats flapping around the house.
Wolves howling in the woods.
Mice scurrying in the house.

Elicia Martin (8)
Kings Court School, Old Windsor

Forest Poem

Walking through the forest,
I can hear birds tweeting overhead.
I feel lost when I am in the forest,
I just can't stop feeling free,
and when I touch a tree,
I feel a shiver down my spine.
When I look ahead,
I see adventures waiting for me.
When I look up into the leaves,
it looks gloomy
and makes me feel sleepy.
When I look into holes in the trees
I see squirrels.
I feel open when I look into the treetops.
I feel a shiver down my spine
as I walk through the forest.
Wolves are howling in the distance.
Owls are flapping their wings
and it echoes very loud.
I can see that the wood goes on
forever and ever.

Aimee Cockburn (7)
Kings Court School, Old Windsor

The Moon

Owls screeching,
flapping wings of furry bats and fluffy owls,
the howling of wolves getting lost in the whirling wind.

Spiky hedgehogs snuffling,
rats squeaking frantically in the wandering night,
cats scratching at the door.

The moon is bright, so bright,
the stars are twinkling,
so light it could almost be day.

Eisha Gandhi (8)
Kings Court School, Old Windsor

The Forest

I can hear wolves howling behind me.
I feel lively.
I see animals watching me.
I can hear voices on the wind.
I feel relaxed.
I see animals watching me.
I see life.
I hear crickets.
I see very large trees.
I hear birds pecking the trees.
I hear birds singing.
I hear water flowing.

Nadiya Ziafat (7)
Kings Court School, Old Windsor

The Moon

Cats running around on the road in the dark, spooky night.
Werewolves howling at the dark night.
Hedgehogs running.

Rats look for something to eat.
The phone rings in the middle of the night but no one's awake.
Wonderful children sleep having brilliant dreams.
Dogs bark, doors swing open.

Foxes are hungry but there's nothing to eat.
Badgers are lonely in the night.

Lauren Correa (8)
Kings Court School, Old Windsor

Seasons

Autumn
Leaves are falling from the trees,
floating along through the breeze.
They make big piles on the ground,
people like to kick them around.

Winter
Snow starts to fall,
let's make a snowball.
You might hear Santa say, 'Ho, ho, ho'
but be careful not to freeze.
I hope you enjoy Christmas Day,
I hope you get lots of presents that special day.

Spring
Spring is the time when the flowers start to grow
and the sun starts shining through the showers.
Also Easter starts when you eat chocolate
and hot cross buns and decorate your bonnet with flowers.
Everyone gets busy with gardening.

Summer
Summer is the time when the leaves turn
a bit darker than spring leaves,
and we get excited because the holidays
start and we get to play.
Everyone ends school on different days
and goes on holiday on different days.

Gemma Sutton (7)
Lewknor CE Primary School, Watlington

The Runaway Tractor

My dad's tractor is still at the top of the hill,
All alone and very still.

So I stepped inside and pushed the gear,
Oh dear! Oh dear! Oh dear!
For pushing the gear and trying to steer,
Felt like drinking too much beer.

My dad said it was a doddle,
But please tell me why it started to wobble?

Down the hill, fast it rolled,
'Remember the handbrake,' I was told!
Still tumbling down the slippery slope,
My tummy really could not cope.
I was beginning to feel quite sick,
I really needed to find the handbrake quick!
I grabbed at a lever to try and keep it still,
But I suddenly realised I'd started to lower the drill!

I'd started to plant in the seed,
It really is the handbrake that I need!

I was feeling very scared now,
I need to stop but I don't know how!

But, hang on, I was slowing and slowing,
The tractor? Well, now it's not going.

'Yes, the diesel's run out, I am so glad,
Now all I've got to do is face my dad,
This could be bad!'

Jack McIntosh (9)
Lewknor CE Primary School, Watlington

My Dog Pepsie

My dog is a cocker spaniel,
Pepsie is her name,
Pepsie is very naughty,
She takes our shoes,
Sits on the table and eats our food.

My dog is like a bottle of pop,
She bubbles and fizzes
And dances around.

When burglars arrive
She makes no sound
And comes to my bed
And lazes around.

My dog Pepsie!

Isabella Carroll (7)
Lewknor CE Primary School, Watlington

Two Little Eggs

Two little eggs
Called Mog and Megs
Had no arms
And had no legs

But they had faces
Smooth and round
One was white
And one was brown

They had eyes
And a mouth and nose
And tasted yummy
Scrambled on toast.

Laura Swain (7)
Lewknor CE Primary School, Watlington

Football Star

I want to be a footballer
it's what I plan to be.
I will be very famous
and you'll see me on TV.

Of course, I would play for Chelsea
cos Chelsea is the best
and I would be so very proud
to wear their bright blue vest.

I intend to be a striker
and score fantastic goals.
I would aim them straight and true
and never hit the poles.

When I'm rich and famous
and drive my red sports car
everyone will wave to me
because I am a star.

David Greensmith (8)
Lewknor CE Primary School, Watlington

The Slippery Match

In the post were some tickets, I was amazed,
I went to the match, I was very glazed.

Then a player slipped over,
I think he tripped over a four-leafed clover!

At the end of the day, I say, 'What a bad match.'
Now all I have to do is sort out my scratch.

Ben McIntosh (7)
Lewknor CE Primary School, Watlington

A Cat And A Rat

I had a little cat,
Who liked to scratch his mat.
Coloured grey with white paws,
He had very sharp claws.
Outside he saw a rat,
Big, black and very fat.
Quick and fast I opened doors,
Then rat was in cat's claws.

Thomas C S Bishop (10)
Lewknor CE Primary School, Watlington

The Mole In The Hole

Put that mole in that hole.
Don't let him out.
Put some lovely lead on top.
Put the small mole in the small hole.
Don't put that mole in that hole,
Let's sell him, why not?
The mole got sold
And his story is told.

Dan Lamb (8)
Lewknor CE Primary School, Watlington

Blue Whales

I love blue whales
But I don't like snails.
Blue whales are blue and grey
And they always know their way.
Krill stain the sea red
And blue whales don't have a bed.

Charlotte Coles (8)
Lewknor CE Primary School, Watlington

The Magic Ballet Shoes

One day I had the most amazing dream.
I dreamt that I found some magic ballet shoes.
I put them on and started to dance away.
I spun and found that I was suddenly the World Champion.
I dreamt that I had won.
The strangest thing was that when I awoke
The ballet shoes were still there on my feet!

Bella Haywood (9)
Lewknor CE Primary School, Watlington

Giraffe

There's a giraffe in my bath.
He got here on a raft.
His name is Kangaroo.
He's got such a lot to do.
He's gone home up the drain.
He said he would come back again.
He lives in a very small tent
In a village in Kent.

Jenny Claire Atterton (9)
Lewknor CE Primary School, Watlington

My Special Sister

My special sister,
She likes to squeal and shout,
When my friends ask me to explain,
I say her batteries have run out.

She can't talk, but she loves to spin,
She's not like me and you,
She likes to live in her own world,
But she's sweet and lovely too.

Faye Baker (9)
Lewknor CE Primary School, Watlington

Time Machine

My dad is an inventor
He invented a time machine
I went into his laboratory
And felt quite keen

I saw all his inventions
I liked the box-shaped one
I thought it was a toaster
So I switched it on

I put a bit of bread in
And tried to find a switch
There was nothing on the toaster
I thought there was a glitch

I went to pick my toast up
It all went very weird
I thought I needed glasses
My toast had disappeared

I tried to get my toast back
By turning a small dial
It all went fuzzy in my eyes
It really was a trial

Something poked me in the dark
I thought, *that's my dad, John*
I opened up my cloudy eyes
And saw an iguanodon!

I backed into a stone cave
It launched a scowl at me
It started eating branches
And then began to flee

I got up from my bottom
And thinking, *what a crime!*
I thought that I was dreaming
I was in a different time

I walked along the swishy grass
And heard a mighty din
My dad was really cross with me
And thought I'd done a sin

Now we're back home again
And everything is fine
We both remember the time machine
But Dad dumped it down a mine!

Jack Hollywood (10)
Lewknor CE Primary School, Watlington

The Rescue

I went to the park today
I shouted a big, 'Hooray'
I saw a man with a dog
Who crashed into a log.

And then the dog did the same
And then the ambulance came
The ambulance took him away
It was a very sad day.

The dog came and gave me a lick
And said, 'My master is sick.'
He saw a wishing well
And wished his master was well.

Tom Hollywood (8)
Lewknor CE Primary School, Watlington

The Girl Who Looked Charming!

There was a young girl called Francesca,
Who was charming and kind,
No court jester.

She was ever so smart,
She loved fashion and art,
How great to have

Such a sister.

Jemima Dutton (9)
Lewknor CE Primary School, Watlington

L'Hiver Blanc

The winter was white this year,
we were worried it would clear,
we got to play day after day,
and the snow never went away.

We made snow angels and a big snowman,
my brother Matt helped me and so did Dan
we ran inside as the snow fell down,
Mum gave us toast that was golden-brown.

We wrapped up warm and ran back out,
there was a fresh blanket of snow and we let out a shout,
the end of the day drew very near,
we went to bed waiting for Santa and his reindeer.

Laura Nunn (10)
Lewknor CE Primary School, Watlington

Giving A Dog A Bath

When you give a dog a bath,
It can be such a laugh.

The dog will dash round and round,
Until you finally track him down.

You can bet,
You will get very, very wet.

He will splash and dash about,
And you might have to give him a clout.

But when it's all finished and done,
You will be his number one.

Amy Miles (9)
Lewknor CE Primary School, Watlington

England Here I Come

Football, cricket, any sport.
They're the games for me.
My dad helps me with the training.
But he always lands on one knee.

I plan to be a professional.
I really want the best.
At the moment it looks quite good
As I think I'm better than the rest.

'Don't be over-confident,'
My mum always used to say to me.
But I don't listen to her,
Because I'm going to play for England one day.

Adam Muttitt (9)
Lewknor CE Primary School, Watlington

The Theme Park

The theme park is exciting,
because of all the rides,
and all the roller coasters
will churn your insides.

Now you may lose your dinner,
and you may cough up bile,
but it's the best day of your life,
so you are sure to smile.

So if you go to the theme park,
(and I do hope you go),
Be sure to go on all the rides,
and your happiness will show!

Charlotte Kotvics (10)
Lewknor CE Primary School, Watlington

Chocolate

Chocolate is my favourite food
It tastes gooey and sweet
It puts me in a cheerful mood
When I'm given it for a treat.

Dairy Milk is the best
The yummiest chocolate in the world
But I don't say 'No' to the rest
Like Kit-Kat, Milky Way or Twirl.

It's brown and sticky
And melts in my mouth
I would eat it every day
If I was allowed!

Holly Sutton (8)
Lewknor CE Primary School, Watlington

My Dog Jess

Bless my Jess
With her silky brown fur
We all love and cherish her
She loves to run
And in the woods she has fun
Bounding through leaves
And chasing round trees
She's sniffing and smelling
And pheasants she's telling
'I am on your way
To come and play!'

Lily May Anson (9)
Lewknor CE Primary School, Watlington

My Little Brother

My little brother is called Stuart
He is very cute and cuddly too
But sometimes he drives my mum crazy
Like when he climbed into the upstairs loo!

My little brother is cheeky
He is learning to climb the stairs
But his favourite trick at the moment
Is climbing on the kitchen chairs.

My little brother is special
I love my little brother a lot
I have four other sisters
But he's the only brother I've got.

Megan Hawkes (9)
Lewknor CE Primary School, Watlington

The Tornado

Watch out! Watch out!
There's a tornado about.
You can hear the people scream and shout!
The animals are in a spin
And they can hear an awful din!
The tornado is shredding everything in its path
And this is really not a laugh!
The tornado is really quite thin
And it's still sucking everything in!
It's stolen my dad's digger
And isn't getting any bigger!

William Notley (8)
Lewknor CE Primary School, Watlington

I Once Went To Sea

I once went to sea, I really did!
Octopus and squid playing on the seabed
Shells and clams hiding in the seaweed

I once went to sea, I really did!
Rainbow fish scattered along the coral reef
Sharks eating krill and tuna

I once went to sea, I really did!
Whales splashing and dolphins leaping
I once went to sea, I really did!

Elisabeth Gowens (8)
Lewknor CE Primary School, Watlington

The Door

Go and open the door
Maybe there is a
Talking cat
That has five eyes.

Go and open the door
Maybe there is a
Kind child
Who has black hair.

Go and open the door
Maybe there is a
New house that talks
And is very, very tall.

The wind is in the sky
It is cold, windy and freezing.

Kathryn Donnelly (8)
Longcot & Fernham CE Primary School, Faringdon

My Family

My dad is a big stuntman,
This means he's really cool.
Jumping from high cliffs
And driving cars that really rule.

My mum's a secret pop star,
Although she says she's not.
I bought her yuck new album,
Sounds like a load of snot!

My sister is a writer,
So many books she's wrote.
They're all about some man,
Named Mr Puny Goat.

I am a secret agent,
009 my name.
Finding lovely ladies,
Is my perfect game.

Michael Brockie (10)
Longcot & Fernham CE Primary School, Faringdon

The Pig

I have a big snout and
a pink, curly tail. I like
to roll around in the mud
and guzzle lots of
food. People think
I'm smelly but I think
I smell nice.

Matthew Davis (9)
Longcot & Fernham CE Primary School, Faringdon

The Door

Go and open the door
Maybe there is a kind princess beckoning
Or maybe there is a bad giant there
He is very sad, angry, evil.

Go and open the door
Maybe there is an evil wizard
Or maybe there is a giant crying
She has green eyes and six warts.

Go and open the door
Maybe there is a wizard
Or maybe there is a wood, which is dark and gloomy
Just go and open the door.

Philippa Sayers (8)
Longcot & Fernham CE Primary School, Faringdon

The Door

Go and open the door
Maybe there's a snake
In Australia.

Go and open the door
Maybe there are bees
Coming to chase you away.

Go and open the door
Maybe there's a monster
That will eat you up.

Go and open the door
Maybe it will be scary
Or maybe it will be Granny.

Freddie Plumb (8)
Longcot & Fernham CE Primary School, Faringdon

The Door

Go and open the door
Maybe there will be an evil scientist,
With orange hair and
Some black trousers.

Go and open the door
There might be a talking dog
That is very chubby
With a piece of bacon.

Go and open the door
Maybe there will be a skeleton,
Hiding behind a rock
With some broken bones near it.

Go and open the door
You will be scared.

Ray Kimber (9)
Longcot & Fernham CE Primary School, Faringdon

Go And Open The Door

Go and open the door
Even if there's gigantic spiders,
Hairy legs going very slowly
Dark smudged black.

Go and open the door
Even if there's a T-rex
With gleaming red eyes
Racing through the black night.

Go and open the door
To happy, jolly Father Christmas
Saying, 'Ho, ho, ho,'
And giving you lots of presents.

Joe Timms (8)
Longcot & Fernham CE Primary School, Faringdon

The Giraffe

In the
  wild
    a
      giraffe
        lives
          in
            Africa
            on the
              plains
                of the
                Masai Mara
              but we see
            them in zoos
            or safari parks.
            They   can   be
            camouflaged. They
          have horns. They are
        yellow   and   brownish
        co   lour. They
        ha   ve long
        le   gs and
        a   long
        n   eck
        th   ey
        li   ke
        ea   ting
        le   av
                          es

Rebecca Miquel Sarjeant (9)
Longcot & Fernham CE Primary School, Faringdon

Dogs

Big

ears.

Dogs

can be

scruffy, dogs

can be smooth,

dogs can be big   il

dogs can be small,   ta

dogs can be skinny, dogs can be fat, but   g's

they are all still dogs. Dogs like running, they   Do

run all day and night. There are lots of different

types of dogs, like Jack Russell and lurchers

whippets and greyhounds . . . but they are all

still dogs. Dogs will eat   Dogs go 'Woof

anything, they will eat   woof, woof

beans,   woof, woof

sausages,   woof, woof''

those   all day

other   and

foods.   it is

They.   ann

drink   oy

water.   ing

Peter Zinovieff (9)
Longcot & Fernham CE Primary School, Faringdon

Yesterday And Today

Yesterday it was sunny
It was boiling.
Today it was snowy.
I am cold.

Yesterday it was hot and I groaned
Because I was boiled.
Today I was really happy
As it was snowy and white.

Yesterday it was hot
And the car groaned.
Today I was going along in white snow
Our car nearly got stuck!

Yesterday the plants were sparkly
And were shrivelling up.
Today they are snowy
And have icicles on them.

Yesterday the paths were brown
And hot.
Today the road and paths
Are white and sparkly.

Yesterday I groaned
Around the playground.
Today I built a snowman
And a big snowball.

Yesterday I was unhappy
About my sunflower.
Today I was excited
And ready to play.

Yesterday I felt unhappy
And sad inside.
Today I was really jolly
And really pleased to see snow.

Andrew Brockie (8)
Longcot & Fernham CE Primary School, Faringdon

The Door

Go and open the door
Maybe there's a wizard,
Or a talking dog,
Or a lovely princess.

Go and open the door
Maybe there's a wizard in a room with red wallpaper,
Or the talking dog is in the park with swings,
Or the princess is in a castle with servants.

Go and open the door
Maybe the wizards are making spells,
Or the talking dog might stare at you,
Or the princess is sitting on the throne.

Go and open the door
Be excited,
Be happy,
Be calm.

Ellesha Bedford (9)
Longcot & Fernham CE Primary School, Faringdon

The Door

Go and open the door,
Maybe there is a ghost
In a haunted house,
Saying, *'Oooooh!'*

Go and open the door,
Maybe there is a princess
In a castle saying,
'Help! Help! I am trapped by the wicked witch.'

Go and open the door
Maybe there is a blue whale
In the blue sea
Saying *'Boob, boob!'*

Isabel Amison (7)
Longcot & Fernham CE Primary School, Faringdon

The Door

Go and open the door,
Maybe there's a kind girl called Daisy,
Waiting to give you chocolate.
She might be very kind.

Go and open the door,
Maybe there's a haunted house,
With ghosts and moving pumpkins,
With horrible webs and spiders.

Go and open the door,
Maybe there are lots of children,
Three helpers and a teacher too,
Maybe the teachers are amazed
And the children stare at you.

Just go and open the door!

Georgia De-Bank (8)
Longcot & Fernham CE Primary School, Faringdon

My Nanny

My nanny loves art and crafts,
My nanny makes yummy cakes.
My nanny makes me smile,
My nanny says funny things.

My nanny's a whiz on the computer,
My nanny is funny on her mobile phone,
My nanny takes me on trips and bus rides,
My nanny takes me to interesting places.

My nanny loses her glasses,
My nanny calls me by the wrong name,
My nanny gives me hugs and kisses,

My nanny is the best and I love her!

Tara Hingston (8)
Longcot & Fernham CE Primary School, Faringdon

The Door

Go and open the door,
Maybe there are dementors,
Or people working, giving you a splitting headache,
or maybe there's a big garden full of flowers.

Go and open the door,
Maybe there is a big lake and darkness and bare trees,
Or even a building site with bendy trees,
Or maybe there are lovely looking trees and flowers.

Go and open the door,
Maybe there will be dementors swamping towards you,
Or even the builders showing their saws to you,
Or maybe there will be birds fluttering towards you.

Maybe it will be misty or foggy,
Or shiny or damp.

Natascha Jane Blesing (7)
Longcot & Fernham CE Primary School, Faringdon

The Solar System

The world seems huge to me,
But it's far from the best,
Compared to the rest,
The sun as big as could be,
But as hot as I know.

Mercury nearest to the sun,
Venus is the bigger one,
Then comes our dear old friend, the Earth,
Then Mars, the red planet.

Jupiter is a big gas planet,
Saturn is a tiny bit smaller than it,
Uranus and Neptune, the twins,
Pluto out there alone,
Cold as could be.

Rosie Frost (9)
Long Lane Primary School, Reading

Love

Love is pink like fluffy hearts,
It smells like perfumed soap,
It tastes like sugar doughnuts,
It sounds like birds singing,
It feels like calm silk,
It looks like a gentle breeze,
It reminds me of Mum cuddling me.

Gregory White (8)
Long Lane Primary School, Reading

Fear

Fear is black like a dark, damp cave.
It looks like a haunted house.
It feels like a stinging scorpion.
It tastes like a stale cake.
It reminds me of a charging rhino.
It smells like an erupting volcano.
It sounds like a howling werewolf.

David Jones (7)
Long Lane Primary School, Reading

Hate!

Hate is red like hot blood.
It feels like burning fire.
It tastes like burnt toast.
It smells like gas fumes.
It reminds me of an angry boar.
It sounds like snorting pigs.
It looks like Growling Griffins.

Jack Lowery (7)
Long Lane Primary School, Reading

Fish

I've never seen a fatter fish
than the one and only pufferfish.
It blows up like a balloon
then goes *kaboom!*

If you pop it with a pin
its insides will come out through its skin.

Everyone will say, 'Yuck!'
when they get covered in muck.

Louie Sims (9)
Long Lane Primary School, Reading

Pets

There are three cats in my house
One cat miaows when he's hungry
One cat always bites
And one cat eats all day.
Okay, he's a bit greedy
And he wants to eat our guinea pigs
He stares at them all day.

Luke Dunkerton (9)
Long Lane Primary School, Reading

Hate!

Hate is red like flaming hot fire.
It tastes like cold beans.
It reminds me of staring people.
It feels like exploding volcanoes.
It looks like fighting children.
It sounds like angry seas.

Megan Yeates (7)
Long Lane Primary School, Reading

Tennis

I am a tennis player as good as can be.
I swing my racket up to my shoulder
And hit the ball as far as can be.
I get a ball and I serve a little shot.
It goes into the net.
I serve again and hit it as far as I can see.
I say I've won the match and hit the ball into the crowd,
And get the trophy.
The crowd goes wild.

Katrina Corrigan (9)
Long Lane Primary School, Reading

Hate

Hate is yellowy-red like flaming bombs
It smells like burning rubber
It tastes like green rotten yoghurts
It reminds me of a wild boar
It looks like an ugly witch
It sounds like a monster growing.

Rhys Frank-Harry (8)
Long Lane Primary School, Reading

Love

Love looks like red roses.
It smells like sweet candy.
It feels like red fire.
It reminds me of Mum.
It sounds like sparkling red flames.

William Muzzelle (7)
Long Lane Primary School, Reading

Art

Art is a gift,
You should treasure it well,
Some artists are swift,
And some aren't so swell,
They take their time,
They sketch it out,
Their paints are fine,
And they sell their pictures throughout.

Aaron Baker (9)
Long Lane Primary School, Reading

School

School is boring,
School is fun,
Whenever you hear someone snoring,
It will be my head teacher who weighs a ton,
All the teachers say, 'Hello.'
We never get told off,
Because they're playing the cello.

Rachel Stout (10)
Long Lane Primary School, Reading

Hate

Hate is blue like the rapid waves.
It looks like a Viking war.
It tastes like rotting fish.
It reminds me of the great fire of London.
It smells like burning gas.

Benn Pickering (7)
Long Lane Primary School, Reading

My Dog Went To Heaven

My dog went to Heaven
Flew up to Devon
And saw Beckham Number 7

Unlike Beckham Number 7
She was smooth, soft and generous.
But when you ate your dinner
You had to shut the door
Because she could not stand food.

Natalie Jones (9)
Long Lane Primary School, Reading

The Internet

www. it's always there,
If you like it or not,
Now for the middle, that's a different case,
It could be tent, it could be lace,
The bit at the end could be .com
It really depends on the website you're on.

The enD.com

Hazel Lupton (9)
Long Lane Primary School, Reading

Weather

Sunny weather is warm and cool,
A great time to jump in the swimming pool.
Snowy weather is cold but great,
You can throw snowballs and even ice-skate.
Rainy weather, he's a tricky fella,
You'll have to bring your coat and umbrella.
Stormy weather, it'll blow you away,
So whatever you do, don't get in its way.

Tadhg Piotrowski (9)
Long Lane Primary School, Reading

Dog

My auntie's getting a new dog,
Her cat is as dead as a log,
We go round to see it,
My little sister buys him a biscuit.

Ten years later we go round again,
Take him for a walk
With two old men.

My uncle and my dad are talking
About getting a monkey,
My auntie says, 'No way.
It would nick the door key.'

The next day her dog dies,
My little sister cries,
She says, 'Will he go to Heaven,
Or even on holiday to Devon?'

Jasmine Stonehewer (9)
Long Lane Primary School, Reading

Anger

Anger makes you mad,
Anger makes you punch,
Anger is something that nobody likes,
Anger makes war,
Anger's sister is peace,
Anger hates the world,
Anger lives in Venus,
His sister lives on Earth,
Anger is evil,
Anger likes fire.

Aaron Slingsby (9)
Long Lane Primary School, Reading

Millie

My nan is getting a new dog,
We're going to the NCDL,
We get inside and the barking is like Hell.
My little sister's crying,
It sounds like someone's dying.
We look around,
No dog my nan fancies, to be found.

We go back to reception,
To say a sad, 'No.'
The lady there says, 'Hey, don't go,
Janie bring in Tillie.'
She says to us, 'I hope you like her, she's so silly!'
In comes a lively black dog,
My nan straightaway says 'Yes!'
We give an almighty cheer
Loud enough for a deaf dog to hear.
We changed her name from Tillie to Millie.
    Silly Millie.

Kaia Bint Savage (9)
Long Lane Primary School, Reading

Dogs

I love dogs whatever they're like
Even if they go for a hike,
Even if they ride a bike,
Even if they're lunatics,
Even if they swallow
A twig and
Even if they
look
like
a
pig!

Joanna Thomas (10)
Long Lane Primary School, Reading

Trampolining

Boing! Boing! You go up high
And it feels like you're flying in the sky,
I love trampolining,
I love going up high
It feels like I'm on a different world
When I'm up there the world looks so small,
I love trampolining, it makes me so happy,
If I could do a back flip,
It would be like being in a Tornado,
When I do a front drop,
It feels like I'm lying in the air then falling to the ground,
Nice and safely.

Jodie Smith (9)
Long Lane Primary School, Reading

My Olympics

An experience of a lifetime,
I met medalists,
The atmosphere was superb
In the stadiums.
The Croatians and Hungarians
Were especially loud!
My favourite sport was horse jumping,
And hockey was fantastic.
An experience of a lifetime.
My experience of a lifetime.

Alistair Haggis (9)
Long Lane Primary School, Reading

The Wall

I climb on the wall,
I fall off the wall,
I call, 'Help, help, get me down.'
Then someone climbs on the wall,
They are really tall.
They dial 999,
And call for an ambulance.
I go to hospital,
They check to see if I've broken something.
They say I am alright,
And I go home.

Marissa Stephens (9)
Long Lane Primary School, Reading

Earth

Round and blue,
green as well.
Animals on land and below the sea.

Sharks and tigers, monkeys and shrimps
and all the other little blimps.

Houses and cars, people as well.
Cats and dogs get in a scrap, crushing plants,
climbing trees, promise you won't tell,
please oh, please!

George Lewington (9)
Long Lane Primary School, Reading

World War II

I am running to the air raid shelter,
I don't know what to do,
I can hear the bombs going off,
And now I need a poo.
My dad's flying a bomber,
My mum's working in a factory,
My brother and I are on Sword Beach,
To help fight the war.

Matthew Tuttle (9)
Long Lane Primary School, Reading

On The Field

Thin air breezing over my head.
The field is fun.
The field is giant.

The leaves blowing in the air.
The field is fun.
The field is giant.

The cow mooing happily in the field nearby.
The field is fun.
The field is giant.

The insects are crawling over the green grass.
The field is fun.
The field is giant.

Harry Oakley (7)
Pangbourne Primary School, Reading

On The Field

The air gives a silent breeze.
The field is fun, the field is natural.

Trees look over everything.
The field is fun, the field is natural.

The hot sun will shine on you.
The field is fun, the field is natural.

Leaves blow in the wind.
The field is fun, the field is natural.

The gazebo is dusty.
The field is fun, the field is natural.

You can swing on the bars.
The field is fun, the field is natural.

The wind will blow on you.
The field is fun, the field is natural.

Olivia Wyndham (7)
Pangbourne Primary School, Reading

On The Field

Tall trees gazing from above.
The field is massive. The field is natural.

Bars for us to play on.
The field is massive. The field is natural.

Grass that's just been cut.
The field is massive. The field is natural.

Gazebo made out of wood.
The field is massive. The field is natural.

Conway O'Neill (8)
Pangbourne Primary School, Reading

The Field

The leaves are crusty and crunchy.
The field is grassy,
The field is fun.

The cows are mooing.
The field is grassy,
The field is fun.

The grass is grassy and slippery.
The field is grassy,
The field is fun.

The insects are buzzing.
The field is grassy,
The field is fun.

Laura Everett (8)
Pangbourne Primary School, Reading

On The Field

Grass is wet and dry.
The field is fun.
The field is good.

The sun is shiny.
The sun is hot.

The grass is slippery.
The grass is sticky.
The grass is muddy.

The trees are waving.
The trees are sticky.

Etham Basden (7)
Pangbourne Primary School, Reading

On The Field

Khaki grass buffeted in the wild.
The field is sunny, the field is wild.

The insects crawl all around.
The field is sunny, the field is wild.

Molehills scattered all around.
The field is sunny, the field is wild.

Sun is shining on the field.
The field is sunny, the field is wild.

Breeze is windy on me.
The field is sunny, the field is wild.

Ryan Paxford (8)
Pangbourne Primary School, Reading

On The Field

The sun is very hot.
The field is green,
The field is fun.
Breeze whispers on my skin.
The field is green,
The field is fun.
The insects are crawling around.
The field is green,
The field is great.
The cows are mooing.
The field is green,
The field is noisy.

Lauren Faulkner (8)
Pangbourne Primary School, Reading

On The Field

Grass smooth as sand.
The field is wet, the field is natural.

Leaves are brittle and light green.
The field is wet, the field is natural.

Insects fly around the field.
The field is wet, the field is natural.

The air smells fresh.
The field is wet, the field is natural.

The sun beaming on my back.
The field is wet, the field is natural.

Amy Lafford (9)
Pangbourne Primary School, Reading

On The Field

The air gives us breeze,
The field is sunny.

Trees look down on us,
The field is sunny.

The gazebo is dusty,
The field is sunny.

The leaves rustle in the breeze,
The field is sunny.

Taylor Stephens (7)
Pangbourne Primary School, Reading

On The Field

The grass is wet and slippery.
The field is fresh, the field is grassy.

The breeze whispers in my ear.
The field is slippery, the field is grassy.

The cows go *moo, moo.*
The field is slippery, the field is grassy.

The air smells fresh.
The field is slippery, the field is grassy.

Ella Jones (7)
Pangbourne Primary School, Reading

On The Field

The leaves
Are twinkling
In the breeze.

The field is massive.
The field is exciting.
The air gives a silent breeze.

The field is massive.
The field is exciting.

Katherine Trew (7)
Pangbourne Primary School, Reading

On The Field

The sun is hot.
The field is great, the field is fun.
The breeze is all around us.
The field is great, the field is fun.
The field is brilliant.
The field is great, the field is fun.

Scott Parker (7)
Pangbourne Primary School, Reading

On The Field

The sun's rays on my back.
The field is muddy, the field is foggy.

The air is blowing fiercely.
The field is muddy, the field is foggy.

The grass is green and fun.
The field is muddy, the field is foggy.

The gazebo shelters from the wind.
The field is muddy, the field is foggy.

Michael Shellard (8)
Pangbourne Primary School, Reading

On The Field

The grass is damp,
The field is wet.
Trees are swaying.
The bars are wet.
The leaves are falling
And the sun is shining.

Tegan Scott (7)
Pangbourne Primary School, Reading

The Field

The sun shining bright on the field.
The field is wet, the field is short.
Insects are digging in the ground.
The field is wet, the field is short.
The grass is glowing in the sun.

Kalila Hayward (8)
Pangbourne Primary School, Reading

On The Field

I can feel the breeze on my arms.
The field is great, the field is fun.

The leaves are blowing in the air.
The field is great, the field is fun.

The cows are mooing in the field.
The field is great, the field is fun.

The gazebo is dusty.
The field is great, the field is fun.

Joe Sumner (7)
Pangbourne Primary School, Reading

Seaside Sounds

We are the children that
paddle in the sea, paddle in the sea.
We are the waves that
crash and splash, crash and splash.
We are the seaweed that
floats on the current, floats on the current.
We are the waves that
crash and splash, crash and splash.
We are the fish that
swim on the bottom, swim on the bottom.
We are the waves that
crash and splash, crash and splash.
We are the sharks that
eat all the fish, eat all the fish.
We are the waves that
crash and splash, crash and splash.
We are the seals that
rescue lost things, rescue lost things.
We are the waves that
crash and splash, crash and splash.

Katriona King (7)
Pluckley CE Primary School, Ashford

What Is Christmas Like?

I'm walking along the pitch-black road,
With only the moon as my guide.
I walk into my tiny thatched cottage.
I hope Christmas will hurry and come soon.
On my door a holly wreath lies; I walk in through the door
To the lovely smell of turkey's greasy thighs.
As I take off my socks and warm my feet,
I smell the lovely juicy meat,
Christmas cake and creamy custard,
Fudge cake and yellow mustard.
I go to the cupboard and take out some marshmallows,
I fork them up, roast them and eat them all like grapes.
Next day comes, I wake so early,
I rush downstairs excitedly, would there be any presents?
Of course! I tear all the wrapping paper off,
I eat all the chocolates and then I cough.
I feel round and fit to burst.
This is what Christmas is like.

Chloe Cohen (9)
Pluckley CE Primary School, Ashford

Seaside Sounds

We are the ships that sail in all weathers,
Sail in all weathers.
We are the waves that spray the rocks,
Spray the rocks.
We are the winds that direct the boats,
Direct the boats.
We are rocks that are hard and cold,
Hard and cold.
We are the waves that crash and splash,
Crash and splash.

Naomi Robinson (7)
Pluckley CE Primary School, Ashford

The Sounds Of The Sea

We are the children that run and shout,
run and shout.
We are the waves that crash and splash,
crash and splash.
We are the seaweed that sways to the beat,
sways to the beat.
We are the waves that crash and splash,
crash and splash.
We are the sea urchins that spike everyone,
spike everyone.
We are the waves that crash and splash,
crash and splash.
We are the boats that bob up and down,
bob up and down.
We are the waves that crash and splash,
crash and splash.

Amber Hurst (8)
Pluckley CE Primary School, Ashford

Royal Albert Hall

I step on the stage, my heart is pumping vigorously,
I look around, my nerves are thumping endlessly,
The crowd roars with excitement,
Tears of amazement throughout the parents,
A sigh of relief at the end of the play,
Applause from the overjoyed audience.

I lay on my cushiony sofa at home,
Dreaming about my day.

Sophie Brandon (10)
Pluckley CE Primary School, Ashford

Lady

My pet dog tastes
Like a chocolate bar,
A smooth outside
And a nutty inside.
My dog smells
Like a musty odour,
Like a towel
That has not been
Washed for years.
She sounds like a barking
Fog horn,
She feels like a fluffy white
Polar bear,
She reminds me of my friend
That I can trust.

Emma Oliver (11)
Pluckley CE Primary School, Ashford

Animals

I love all animals, big and small,
Elephants, guinea pigs, short and tall.
Robins red and magpies grey,
Horses eating sweet dry hay.
Ants that scuttle round and round,
Foxes roaming through the town.
Labradors and tabby cats,
Stripy badgers, desert rats.
Dolphins swimming and flicking their tails,
Fluffy hamsters, slugs and snails.
I could go on until I age,
But I'd never fit them all on the page!

Harriet Washer (10)
Pluckley CE Primary School, Ashford

Lottie

My dog is called Lottie,
She has a black and light pink nose,
Lottie is a mad puppy.

Lottie is black and white.
My dog reminds me of a rat,
My dog feels like a rat too.

She has brown eyes.
Lottie is as nice as chocolate chip ice cream,
She has a favourite food and it is meat.

You can tell my dog is a girl because she has a pretty little face.
My dog has long, white whiskers.
Lottie makes a yapping noise at night.

Naomi Bottle (9)
Pluckley CE Primary School, Ashford

Spain

In Spain it was very hot,
The sky was blue,
The sand was golden,
The sea was warm,
Like one massive bath.
The waves were huge,
We had so much fun.
The food was great
In the beach restaurant.

James Larkin (10)
Pluckley CE Primary School, Ashford

Tranquillity

Dolphins doing somersaults
In the tropical sunset,
Before they drop back
Into the sapphire blue, cool, clear water.
The calm waves beating the shore,
The sound is so relaxing.
The sound of the rustle in the coconut tree,
The sound of waves far and near,
Like a horse cantering towards me.
The spongy foam circles my ankles
As I wade further and further in.
I close my eyes for a couple of minutes,
A shiver goes down my spine.
I swim off to meet my dolphin friends.

Charlotte Tyrrell (10)
Pluckley CE Primary School, Ashford

Bentley

My dog.
He is black like
Liquorice All Sorts.
When he sees the black cat
From next door,
He jumps on the window sill and barks!
He likes eating the cat's dinner, 'Mmm, yum!'
He thinks he'd like to sit on the sofa,
So you have to sit on the floor!
His name is
Bentley!

Megan Hill (11)
Pluckley CE Primary School, Ashford

Splashing Rain

I landed on the ground.
I waited.
The smell of Chinese food
Came wafting out
Of a house nearby.
Shadow came over me,
An eagle crossing the moon.
Laying on the fresh corn,
Splashes of rain came dropping
Down on my face.
I watched the stars disappear
Until the morning came.
The warmth on my face
Got even hotter
When the sun came out.
The world fell silent.
Who am I? I'm from the sky.

Sam Bridgeman (10)
Pluckley CE Primary School, Ashford

Australia

Australian town.
Busy market,
Hot sun shining.
Inside cool air conditioning is on full blast.
Outside in the garden, prawns ever so big
Are cooking on the barbecue.

Outback Australia.
Deep in the rainforest, Aborigines
Are hunting for food.
Back at camp, people are playing didgeridoos.
Out in the wild, kangaroos are jumping,
Koalas are chewing eucalyptus trees,
Wombats are lying in the sun.

Amy Gibbons (9)
Pluckley CE Primary School, Ashford

Seasons

There are four different seasons
That change throughout the year,
All of them are special,
But one to me is dear.

In spring all the plants are growing,
And on the grass the dew is glistening,
Now sunshine is just getting ready
For summer's picnics and we'll all start whistling.

In summer the sun blazes
And my skin reddens and burns,
I play games with my friends
And we lick melting ice creams in turns.

Leaves fall from multicoloured trees
On the frosty autumn days,
While my friends and I
Are smashing conkers through the sun's rays.

But best of all I've saved for last,
The joyous Christmas month.
When the lakes all freeze over
And the ice-cold snow covers the trees in triumph.

Lewis Hawkes (10)
Pluckley CE Primary School, Ashford

Colours And Feelings

Red is for a hungry fire,
Blue is for sadness like falling out with friends,
Green is for happiness like swaying grass,
Purple is for a clap of thunder,
Black is for death, as doomed as a stone,
Yellow is for love, like the stars up above.

Christopher Wood (10)
Pluckley CE Primary School, Ashford

What I Did Not Get For Christmas

I did not get an Xbox,
I did not get money.
I did not get a trip to the zoo,
I did not get a monkey.
I did not get a house for Christmas,
I did not go to Spain.
I did not get a fight with a bull,
I did not get an aeroplane.
These are some things I didn't get,
But I did get a quad bike!

Jack Barton (9)
Pluckley CE Primary School, Ashford

My House

My house is a house that shakes.
My house is a house that is noisy.
My house is a house that falls to pieces.
My house is a house that is mad!

My garden is a garden that gets wrecked.
My garden is a garden that is overgrown.
My garden is a garden that's like a battlefield!
My garden is a garden that is full of danger.
All because of my brother!

Justin Bowden (9)
Pluckley CE Primary School, Ashford

Snow

S now is cold and wet but it is also soft like silk,
And sparkles like crystals in the moonlight.

N ow there's something you can do with snow
That really is quite fun. All you have to do is
Make a ball and throw it at someone.

'O h Mum, can I go out to play?
'OK, but wrap up warm, it's really very cold out there
And you'll get frostbite if you fall.'

W hen I go out to play I make snow angels that
Glisten in the sun. The snow is so much fun.

Devon Osborne (9)
Pluckley CE Primary School, Ashford

Autumn

Blow winds, blow,
Soaring up in the sky they go,
Swirling and twirling round,
Until they all fall down to the ground.
All the trees are loudly creaking,
All the men are gently sweeping.
The leaves are flying away to another autumn's day.
Blow winds, blow,
Up the leaves go.

Isobel Emblem (10)
Pluckley CE Primary School, Ashford

Anteater

One day I went to the zoo.
I went through the gate,
It smelt like rotten stew.
I walked a mile,
Tripped over a stile,
With my head stuck in the ground,
My heart started to pound.
Something hairy,
It might be scary,
Picked me up.
It was an anteater, how cute.
'Hello Anteater, here's a newt.'
He ate it.
'Yuk, it's disgusting,' he said,
'I will eat you like apple pie.'
Then I woke up in my bed,
Safe and sound with my sleepy head.
'Hurry up, you look like a fool.
Come on, come on, you'll be late for school.'

Rebekah Holmes (9)
Pluckley CE Primary School, Ashford

Football

F eet are like jelly before we start.
O ff we go, the whistle has blown.
O ff up the pitch I go, sprinting like a cheetah.
T rip over the ball, never mind I got it!
B all is with me, what shall I do?
A rnold is waiting on the other side.
'L eg it up the pitch,' he cried.
L es tackled me, so quickly I shot, I scored! *Hooray!*

Daniel Hills (9)
Pluckley CE Primary School, Ashford

My Special Friend

My special friend is called Jen.
She looks like Matilda,
Black, straight hair.
She is as small as a mouse,
With a roar as loud as an elephant.
When she laughs she snorts like a pig.
She lives in my street. Lives at number two.
We play hide the ball or hide-and-seek.
Jen always forgives me when we argue.
Jen is my special friend.

Matthew Fairchild (9)
Pluckley CE Primary School, Ashford

Mountains

Mountains are big,
Mountains are high,
The tips of mountains touch the sky,
From the Alps to the Himalayas
And Rockies too.
Skiing, snowboarding and chocolate fondue.
My favourite mountain is El Capitan,
I went to see it with my old man.

The snow is white,
The wind is cold,
The happy, smiling faces, young and old.
The whizzing sounds of skis zipping down the mountains.
The streams and fountains trickling down
And the people having snow fights,
Spinning round and round.

Michael Glenn (10)
St Andrew's School, Reading

The Park

In a wood many miles away is a park.
This park is no ordinary park,
It's a silent, most mysterious park,
With a most eerie sound in the night.
I watched it with a growing interesting mood,
Then suddenly with a strange noise, two dozen men appeared.
They went towards goals with a ball in two people's hands.
When they came closer, I saw they had two different shirts on,
One red and white, the other blue. I didn't know what to do.
Then the goalie for blue turned round and looked me straight
in the eye.
He shouted to the rest of his team,
Who ran up to me looking like World War I veterans.
They asked me if I wanted to play.
I said, 'Yes please, but not too rough.'
I played quite well, but they were good.
I was a young boy back then.
I think I'll go back again!

Bertie Marks (10)
St Andrew's School, Reading

Unhealthy

Sweets are yummy,
And sweets are gummy.
Liquorice, Smarties and Allsorts too.
The ones I don't like I flush down the loo!
Oh don't forget those fizzy drinks,
The ones that make your tongue go pink.
The green ones, blue ones,
Yellow ones as well,
But still I think they all taste rather *swell!*

Claire Noakes (10)
St Andrew's School, Reading

Dogs

Dogs can be cuddly,
But some may be fierce.
You can get lots of breeds.
Labradors are my thing,
But I like more,
But some of them are a bore.
I prefer the fluffy ones,
But I don't mind the other ones.

They are just dogs,
Let's not forget the others.
There are cats, hamsters and guinea pigs,
But I prefer dogs,
Dogs are the best,
They are always a friend.

Ysabel Brown (10)
St Andrew's School, Reading

Little Girl Sally

Little girl Sally
Sat on a step
And pouted.

Little girl Sally
Cried
And tears sprouted.

Little girl Sally
Screamed and yelled,
'I just ate a gnat.'

Little girl Sally
Cried and cried
And that was the end of that.

Sophie Meadows (10)
St Andrew's School, Reading

The Metal Fly

One day at school I was having lunch,
When suddenly I heard a rather large crunch.
I looked at my pie
And half a metal fly
Looked up at me and started to cry.
The other half,
Prodding into my calf,
Burst through, joined up and started to laugh.
I flicked it away
Onto Mrs McKay.
It bounced off and landed on a pile of hay.
It called its mates,
Who smashed the plates
And everything else, until they reached their fates.

Stuart Cummings (10)
St Andrew's School, Reading

Nuclear Bombs

The plane passes over making a buzzing sound,
It drops the bomb and the bomb hits the ground.
The people run away from the bomb,
But unfortunately the chase lasted very long.
The people begin to get very tired,
They're worried that they're going to get fried.
The colours blaze, orange, yellow and red,
And suddenly the people are dead.
But the bodies are nowhere to be found,
They're probably buried under the ground.
And on that day, a lot of blood was shed,
And the bombs will keep falling till everyone's dead.

Alfie Walker (10)
St Andrew's School, Reading

Sadness

Clear sky is tear blue, like sadness.
An empty land with wind in the trees is like sadness.
Sadness tastes as if it was salty, misty, cold water.
Sadness is as small and single as a daisy in a meadow.
A pale, misty, lonely ghost is like sadness.
Sadness feels like cold, hollow ice against my skin.
Fresh flowers on a smooth gravestone remind me of sadness.

Edward Reeve (9)
St Mary's School, Henley-on-Thames

Fear

Fear is black, like a black cat.
Fear sounds like the howling of a wolf.
Fear tastes like rice pudding.
Fear is a murderer in London City.
Fear feels like blood and death.
Fear makes me feel sad and it reminds me of a horrible murder.

Benedict Turner (9)
St Mary's School, Henley-on-Thames

Sadness

Sadness is a tear, blue as the clear sky.
Sadness is wind blowing in a lonely and silent land.
Sadness tastes like misty, cold water.
Daisies are in a lonely field of sadness.
Sadness is like a pale, misty ghost.
Sadness is ice melting.
Sadness is flowers from graveyards.

Tilly Pudwell (9)
St Mary's School, Henley-on-Thames

Fear

Fear is black like an unlucky, sad, black cat.
Fear sounds like a long, held-in howl of a wolf.
Fear tastes like a gooey, stodgy rice pudding.
Fear smells like cowpat and mixed sick on the pavement.
Fear looks like a petrified murderer seeing me in the alley.
Fear feels like the pouring blood of a horrible death.
Fear reminds me of when I was in a zoo
And the alligator escaped, with me frightened of it.

Jack Dent (9)
St Mary's School, Henley-on-Thames

Fear

Fear sounds like a hungry tiger crawling through my fear.
Fear tastes like liver in sickening black pudding.
Fear smells like an old yellow cowpat.
Fear is black and unlucky, like a black cat.
Fear feels as if I was stabbed and dying.
Fear reminds me of the day my helpless cat was given away.

Emily Carr (9)
St Mary's School, Henley-on-Thames

Sadness

Sadness is clear blue, like the sky.
Sadness sounds like wind on an empty, lonely, silent land.
Sadness is a daisy in a lonely meadow.
Sadness is a lonely, pale, misty ghost.
Sadness is like cold, melting, hollow ice.
Fresh flowers on a smooth gravestone remind me of sadness.

Anna Burrows (9)
St Mary's School, Henley-on-Thames

Anger

Anger is a blood-red rose.
Anger sounds like yelling in your head, over and over.
Anger tastes like a sour sweet that stings your mouth.
Anger smells like Marmite and rotten milk.
Anger looks like a burning red, scorching hot, orange ball of fire.
Anger feels like sitting on a bed of stinging nettles.
Anger makes you think of people yelling, stopping for a minute,
Then starting again.

Joelle Poulos (9)
St Mary's School, Henley-on-Thames

Fear

Fear is like a tiger creeping through the woods.
Fear is an unlucky black cat.
Black, sickening pudding; that is how fear tastes.
Fear smells like cowpat on the streets of London.
Fear is as if you are looking at a murderer at work.
Fear feels as if you're in the Atlantic Ocean experiencing
                                        a slow, painful death.
Fear reminds you of the times you were helpless and sorry.

Annie Heskin (9)
St Mary's School, Henley-on-Thames

Anger

Anger is as red as a prickly, peaceful rose.
Anger sounds like elephants stampeding in my head.
Anger tastes like sour, gooey liquorice.
Anger is sour, mouldy, sweaty feet.
Anger looks like a blood-red ring of fire.
Red-hot, anger feels like daggers going straight through my heart.
Anger makes me think of sparks coming out of eyes.

Kathryn Venables (10)
St Mary's School, Henley-on-Thames

Anger

Anger is a deadly fire.
Anger sounds weird and fearsome, like a devil.
Anger smells like Marmite and of milk.
Anger is a dead scary devil!
Anger feels like a dagger in your lung.
Anger reminds me of when we moved to England.

Callum Glass (9)
St Mary's School, Henley-on-Thames

Henry VIII

Henry VIII was a very big man,
His tummy was as big as a frying pan.
He wore a hat upon his head
And kept it on when he went to bed.
As Henry started to have his doze,
The feather came down and tickled his nose.
He laughed and laughed until he awoke
And thought somebody had played a joke.
'Who did that?' the big king roared.
He jumped out of bed and picked up his sword.
Nobody was there when he looked round the room,
It was very dark and he fell over a broom.
'Ouch, that hurt,' he said to himself,
But as he stood up he hit his head on a shelf.
He crawled on the floor back to his bed
And felt the wound on his head.
And as he put his hand up there
He felt the feather next to his hair.
'Oh what a silly man am I!'
And began to laugh until he cried.
'The feather from my hat gave me the fright.
I forgot to take it off tonight!'

Catharine Ackford (7)
St Michael's Easthampstead CE (Aided) Primary School, Bracknell

The Tickle Monster

When I wake up in the morning,
The tickle monster is hiding.
Then when I go into my mum's room,
Into her bed I start sliding.

That's when the tickle monster jumps out
Onto the bed and starts tickling.
I'm very, very ticklish,
So I can't stop giggling.

Then it tickles and tickles and tickles,
And tickles and tickles and tickles even more,
So I wriggle and wriggle and wriggle,
And wriggle and wriggle and wriggle towards the door.

But I never actually break free,
Until the monster stops and lets go.
Because the tickle monster is my mum,
And she's only saying hello.

Charlie Johnson (9)
St Michael's Easthampstead CE (Aided) Primary School, Bracknell

Down, Down

Down, down,
Yellow and brown,
Leaves are falling
On the ground.

Down, down,
Gold and brown,
Conkers are bouncing
On the ground.

Down, down,
Wet and round,
Rain is splashing
On the ground.

Emma Rowden (8)
St Michael's Easthampstead CE (Aided) Primary School, Bracknell

Colours

What is red?
Apples and leaves are red -
Hearts and ladybirds are red too.

What is brown?
Tree trunks and pencils are brown -
Chocolate and hair are too.

What is green?
Eyes and grass are green -
Grasshoppers and apples are too.

What is orange?
Sunsets and oranges are orange -
Petals and the sun are too.

What is black?
The night and darkness are black -
Shoes and scarves are too.

These are autumn colours!

Beth Seymour (8)
St Michael's Easthampstead CE (Aided) Primary School, Bracknell

I Went To The Seaside

I went to the seaside and I saw a great big wave,
My grandad bought me a surf board with the money that I'd saved.
Then I surfed all afternoon with my new friend called Millie,
I kept on falling off my board and Millie thought it was silly.

Hanna Edwards (7)
St Michael's Easthampstead CE (Aided) Primary School, Bracknell

My Aunty

My aunty's like a butterfly,
Fluttering here and there,
If you get in her way,
She tickles you everywhere.
She's soft, cuddly and delicate,
That's why I love her!

But when she's angry
She's like a roaring lion,
She roars and roars at me.
Then when she's calmed down,
She's cool and relaxed,
Like a trickling waterfall.

Lauren Owen (9)
St Michael's Easthampstead CE (Aided) Primary School, Bracknell

My Simile Poem

A man with no love
Is like a dark hallway.

A man with no clothes
Is like a tree with no leaves.

A woman with no hair
Is like a leaf with no colour.

A window with no glass
Is like a hat with no feather.

A video with no tape
Is like a banana with no skin.

Jason Slyfield (9)
St Michael's Easthampstead CE (Aided) Primary School, Bracknell

Rainbow

Imagine if a rainbow was *spotted.*
Imagine if a rainbow was *dotted*
Like a colourful Dalmatian
Walking by some plantation,
Oh wouldn't it be a sight to see?

Imagine if the rainbow was completely *red.*
All the other colours had gone to *bed.*
Like a red, red rose,
With a smell that goes up your nose,
Oh wouldn't it be a sight to see?

Spotted or *dotted* or *red,*
I'm just glad the rainbow's *striped.*

Hayley Kennard (8)
St Michael's Easthampstead CE (Aided) Primary School, Bracknell

The Seasons

Trees take off their clothes
Showing off their lovely bark
To the autumn breeze.

Winter now looks up,
Leaves get into winter coats
Made of silver glow.

Chicks pop out their heads
To look at the lovely world
And the spring sunshine.

Summer has arrived,
Clouds part to let through sunshine,
Ice-pops to cool down.

Hannah Boyle (9)
St Michael's Easthampstead CE (Aided) Primary School, Bracknell

My Dad

My dad runs around,
My dad jumps up and down.
No matter what, he never stops
Running around breaking pots.
Playing games, chillin' out
When he's not, he's lulling about.
Although he's mad . . .
He's still my dad!

Philippa Bowden (9)
St Michael's Easthampstead CE (Aided) Primary School, Bracknell

Touch

Touch!
What can you feel?
The splash of a frog jumping on me,
The raindrops falling on me.

Touch!
What can you feel?
The fluff of a dog blowing on me,
Slimy fish splashing on me.

Sophie Javadi-Babreh (7)
Sacred Heart RC Primary School, Henley-on-Thames

Touch!

Touch!
What can you feel?
The wiggly worm
Of a muddy path,
The hairy chick
Of a feathery scarf.

Callum Butler (7)
Sacred Heart RC Primary School, Henley-on-Thames

Touch!

Touch!
(What can you feel?)
The pitter-patter
Of a rain cloud dropping on me,
The falling leaves in the air
Coming from the tree.

Touch!
(What can you feel?)
The wrinkly skin
Of an old man,
The wriggly jelly
Of a metal pan.

Dinu Popa (7)
Sacred Heart RC Primary School, Henley-on-Thames

Touch

Touch!
(What can you feel?)
The black and white dog
Of a happy boy,
The friendly, playful
Football toy.

Touch!
(What can you feel?)
The stinging wasps
Of a horrible nest,
The scary, sick,
Pollen test.

Daniel Cridland (8)
Sacred Heart RC Primary School, Henley-on-Thames

Touch

Touch!
What can you feel?
The prickly skin
Of a shy hedgehog,
The soft velvet petals of a flower,
Like a little brown dog.

Touch!
What can you feel?
The rough outside
Of an arrow head,
The boiling hot sun
That's normally red.

Myfanwy Mountford (7)
Sacred Heart RC Primary School, Henley-on-Thames

Touch

Touch!
What can you feel?
Prickly spikes
Of a spiky hedgehog,
The bouncing body
Of a frog.

Touch!
What can you feel?
The smashing noise
Of a broken glass,
The crunchy volume
Of the smooth, cool grass.

Callum Hilton (7)
Sacred Heart RC Primary School, Henley-on-Thames

The Cool, Mad Cat Rap

I decided late on Sunday
That I would sleep till half-past Monday.
All of a sudden I felt a tap
That awoke me from my nap.
I awoke and there before me
Was a dog jumping around me.
Leave my bed and me to sleep,
I don't even want a peep.
When I ran outside,
I noticed that he was still inside,
So I locked the door behind,
When I remembered there was a flap,
I gave myself a slap.
I went to an alley
Where the tough cats dally,
I would be a little nuts
To hang around these stupid mutts,
So I turned around
And found myself on the ground.
One of the cats tripped me up,
Now I'm going to make him shut up.
I rapidly swung my fists at him,
So I could hurt him.
He pulled out his claws,
That made me run back indoors.
I found the dog in my bed,
He growled at me and I said,
'I'll be better off with the cat instead.'

Oliver Mackinnon (10)
Sandwich Junior School, Sandwich

The Way Michael Became A Football Player

On the way to school
Michael came to school,
We did not like him
Because he is a show off.

Mr B went over to Michael
And said,
'Stop being a show off!'
He said, 'No.'

Mr B said, 'You want to be in the team?
Do not be a show off then!'
'No, it is because
I like being in the team.'

'Are you coming to football?'
'Yes I'm coming,
Because I like football.'

'I like you, sometimes
you can be nasty,
but you are a good football player.'

'Thank you Michael.'
'That is OK, Mr B.
I want to stay
At the school.'

'You cannot be
At the school
Because you will not
Learn any more.'

Jack Venner (10)
Sandwich Junior School, Sandwich

Man U

M an U are the best
A ll over the world we hear their name
N ot Arsenal, United
C hampions of the world 1999
H e's scored on his debut
E veryone knows them
S even is the number of Ronaldo
T en is the number of Van Nistelrooy
E veryone knows them
R oy Keane is the captain.

U nited, United, United
T hey're the best in the world
D on't lose a game.

R is for Ronaldo,
O is for Old Trafford,
N is for nutmeg,
A is for Sir Alex Ferguson, manager of Man U,
L is for learn to play football,
D is for danger of Man U,
O is for *our* team.

N is for Neville,
E is for everyone loves them,
V is for Van Nistelrooy,
I is for injury in the stadium,
L is for last minute when we score,
L is for Liverpool, our rivals,
E is for everyone who plays.

Thomas Skirrow (10)
Sandwich Junior School, Sandwich

Football And Footballers

F ootball, the greatest sport of all.

O ver the moon when your team wins the cup with a cracker
of a goal

O ooo, ah, ooo, the loud sound of the teams' supporters
deafening a deaf person.

T hierry Henry, the best player in the premiership and also
the top scorer with 30 goals.

B ad players get sent off when they have got two yellows,
or when they do an horrendous tackle. Boo!

A rsenal, the champions of the premiership, also known as
The Untouchables.

L osers like Wolves never win.

L ucky Man Utd score on the 90th minute in every game
because they've got Rooney.

R ipping up defenders so they go red in the face
and beg for no more humiliation.

E ssential goals and brilliant crosses.

Y oung star of the future with skill.

E xterminating defences with power, pace and composure.

S parkling crosses, goals and teeth.

H orror for defenders,

E ssential curling crosses,

N ever gets sent off in the premiership,

R ipping up defences,

Y es, Henry scores a cracker of a goal.

C unning tackles from defence,

O le, ole, ole, ole, Cole gets the crowd going.

L ong, beautiful balls, precise from the start.

E xcitement mounts as he comes onto the pitch.

Alex Cowan (10)
Sandwich Junior School, Sandwich

Cats And Dogs And Squirrels, Then The Foxes

C uddly, soft animal that snuggles up to you,
A nd a noisy and hungry animal
T oo tall or too . . .
S mall.

A nd the
N aughty
D ogs are here!

D ogs can be big or small,
O h just look at his lovely coat.
G osh he looks nice as a puppy or a dog.
S o that is how I like cats and dogs!

A nd the
N aughty
D efying squirrels have come out!

S quirrels are cute and
Q uiet and can sometimes be
U nseen.
I t goes from tree to tree and is
R eally
R eally
E qually
L ovely and cute
S quirrels.

T hen
H ere
E qually
N aughty

T errifying foxes that you can
H ear
E qually

F oxes are terrifying.
O h no, run!
X -ray in its brain,
E xtremely frightening,
S o keep running away from foxes.

Jessica Dymott (10)
Sandwich Junior School, Sandwich

Wild Animals

F ast and cunning
O pening his loud, snapping mouth,
X -raying its prey.

B ig hairy beast
E ating raw meat
A te a deer whole
R eady to hunt again.

S lithering through the grass
N aked but its skin
A ppalled by how many rats live
K ills its victim with its tail
E ats twenty rats a day.

R acing down the road
A te an apple for tea
B attered and bruised from the run
B ut still he runs and runs.
I ll he is,
T ill he falls and dies.

A te an orange for tea.
P eter, my friend, is an orang-utan.
E at an ape for tea.

C olours are what we turn into.
H ard, soft, we don't care what colours we are.
A rched back like the London Bridge.
M outh very small, but beaky.
E at loads of leaves every day.
L ife we have like all animals in this world.
E very creature can't see me in the tree.
O nions we hate, just like meat.
N ever go on the ground, that's our golden rule.

Adam Cox (10)
Sandwich Junior School, Sandwich

The Bog Of Doom

In Sunnydale High there is a bog, a bog of doom,
Named after the other bog which chucked them out of the bathroom.
But this bog eats you up when you flush it.
On Wednesday 1999, a boy called Joshua
Discovered that the bog eats you up
So he never goes to the toilet at school, instead he wets himself.
Everyone laughs because they see his cheeks go red
And the person who sits next to him
Can see Joshua's chair covered with wee.
The next morning five students went missing.
Joshua knew what was going on,
This was the job for Joshua, Private Eye.
The boy wasn't scared of anything and would
Stand up to anything or anyone.
He knew someone or something. Of course, it's the Bog of Doom.
'The bog of what?' said Mr Smelly-Breath.
'Doom,' Joshua said in a rather scared way.
''The Bog of Doom's taking our students away,
So I will risk my life to go and see this beast.'
Joshua sounded really confident.
When he went, blood was all over the wall and on the toilet seat.
He took his magnifying glass out and looked at the bog
And he saw some eyes open and they were forcing Joshua
to pull the chain.
Then it happened. Josh was flushed down.
He got dizzy because he was getting swirled around
And he landed on skeletons.
He looked around and found Mrs Arty, the art teacher.
She and Joshua would die in at least five hours.
Mrs Arty and Joshua wandered around.
As they were walking, they noticed that they were the only two,
All the other people were dead.
Two hours have been, only three to go.
Those two were scared out of their wits.
Two more hours gone, and one to go.

Then they saw a black object that was quite rusty.
'A bomb!' Josh said.
Ten seconds to go. 10, 9, 8, 7, 6, 5, 4, 3, 2, 1, *boom!*
They're skeletons!

David Hands (10)
Sandwich Junior School, Sandwich

Autumn Is . . .

Autumn is going back to school
Or even starting a new one.
Autumn is learning more about things
And making new friends at school.

Autumn is when leaves
Fall off trees and turn crispy brown.
Autumn is when animals start to hibernate
And gather their food for the long winter!

Autumn is about harvest festivals
When we give food to the poor.
Autumn is about Hallowe'en
When you have friends to celebrate.

Autumn is about bonfire night
When you eat and drink lots of yummy food.
Autumn is when birds gather food
And fly to hot countries.

Autumn is when it starts to get frosty
And dew settles on the grass.
Autumn is when flowers start to die
And bushes are full of red berries.

Katherine Belsey (8)
Sandwich Junior School, Sandwich

The Naughty Art Stationary

Art is wonderful,
Art is great,
But I wouldn't like to
Eat it on a massive plate.

I like art,
Art likes me,
The paint brushes
Paint a tree.
The Pritt Stick's glue
The big picture of ted,
Now the pencils
Have coloured him in red.

Art is wonderful,
Art is great,
But I wouldn't like to
Eat it on a massive plate.

The felt likes the pens,
The pens like the felt,
And the Scottish shape
Is wearing a red kilt.
The pastels are skidding
Along the blue paper,
The cards are also
Chasing the green stapler.

It's glorious,
It's fabulous,
It's fantastic,
It's extraordinary,
It's unbelievable,
It's spectacular,
It is art!

Taylor Smith (10)
Sandwich Junior School, Sandwich

Pets

M ice are so cuddly,
O h a mouse is so great
U nlike a mouse, we sleep at night
S o when you see a mouse, look after it
E ver get a mouse, do not get a cat.

D ogs are so great
O h a dog will play with you every day
G et a dog and call it Bob.

F ast and cunning
O pening its huge mouth
X -ray in its brain.

B ird flies high in the sky
I t lands and eats worms
R eally hard to see when way up in the sky
D rinks lots of water.

C ats have nine lives
A cat always survives
T iny cats always stay with their mums.

T iger always growls
I t's always on the prowl
G ets its dinner
E very day it climbs through the grass
R unning through the jungle

R ats run up and down the swamp
A nimals that have fleas
T otally covered in mud.

L ions are vicious
I met a lion
O h it will kill you
N obody can kill a lion.

Adam Pope (10)
Sandwich Junior School, Sandwich

My Family

My dad is very happy,
He buys me lots of treats,
But sometimes he gets angry
And terrifies me!

My mum is very nice,
She gives me cuddles at night,
But sometimes she is such a nag,
Always saying, 'Do this . . . do that!'

My brother is very kind,
He picks me up from clubs,
But sometimes he is nasty
And turns my toys into rags!

So altogether my family are OK,
We all have so much fun,
Every single day!

Chloe Cole (9)
Sandwich Junior School, Sandwich

All Ages

When I was 1 I ate a plum,
When I was 2 I had a tissue,
When I was 3 I had a pea,
When I was 4 I swept the floor,
When I was 5 I ate a chive,
When I was 6 I collected some sticks,
When I was 7 I believed in Heaven,
When I was 8 I had a gate,
When I was 9 I had a shine,
When I was 10 I had a pen.

Christina Page (9)
Sandwich Junior School, Sandwich

Autumn Is . . .

Autumn is conkers, glossy, gleaming, polished, pearly,
Smooth as silk, conquerors of other conkers.
Autumn is harvest, when we give old people food
Because they can't get to the supermarket
And it's like so that they will be grateful for us doing something.
Autumn is hibernation, when all little creatures, little ants,
Tortoises, snakes, squirrels and many others sleep.
It's the season that they eat as much as they can
And go to sleep for a month. (How could they do that?)
Autumn is migration, the season when all birds
All go on the rail and fly south.
Autumn is leaves, when they turn a ruby-red colour
And a jewelled-green colour.
Autumn is Hallowe'en, where you scare the people out of their pants
And shout, 'Trick or treat' and lob eggs at your mates.
Autumn is morning dew, where there is a
Coating of beautiful green jewels.

James Igglesden (8)
Sandwich Junior School, Sandwich

Autumn Is . . .

Autumn is when leaves fall off trees
And people stand on them.
Autumn is when the days get shorter
And nights get longer.

Autumn is when we go back to school
Or start a new school.
Autumn is when we put the heating on
To get nice and warm.

Autumn is when animals hibernate
And find warmth.
Autumn is when we get shiny conkers
From horse chestnut trees.

Rachel Barclay (9)
Sandwich Junior School, Sandwich

Autumn Is . . .

Autumn is the beginning of a rough and windy season
With birds searching for food.
Autumn is a time of thick dew
Settling on the frosty grass!

Autumn is the time for conkers to start falling
As the brown covers their rough insides.
Autumn is the time when animals start to hibernate
And when leaves turn brown.

Autumn is a time when we light the sky with fireworks
And eat marshmallows, jacket potatoes and drink hot chocolate.
Autumn is when we give a little food to the elderly
And have harvest festivals.

Autumn is when particular birds start to fly south
Looking for warmer weather.
Autumn is a time when children
Jump in scattering leaves and get dirty.

Autumn is grey, misty clouds,
Bursting to give massive thunder storms.
Autumn is when purple-yellowish leaves
Start gently floating down to the ground.

Autumn is Hallowe'en!
When we go around saying, 'Trick or treat.'
Autumn is when we go back to school
And get a new teacher!

Autumn is a time when we
Start to light fires.
Autumn is a time when we celebrate
Harvest, Hallowe'en and bonfire night!

Elliott Burns (8)
Sandwich Junior School, Sandwich

My Big Brother

My brother can be a bit of a laugh
Although he doesn't let me in the bathroom
When he's having a bath.

He can be nice and he can be nasty,
But when he's nice he plays with me
And takes me places I want.

And when he's nasty, he beats me up
And doesn't let me do anything
I want to do.

He's got his own auto-grass racing mini
And he can drive it
And he's only 13.

When we went to Menorca
I could not afford something that I wanted to buy
So he bought me it.

When we were in Menorca
He taught me how to swim
And go down very deep.

We sometimes save up for games
That we've seen in an Xbox magazine
Or in a games shop.

I like my big brother and I hope he likes me too,
Because he's my big brother,
I do like him, I do.

Grant Hammet (9)
Sandwich Junior School, Sandwich

Autumn Is . . .

Autumn is back to school,
A new class, maybe even a new teacher!
Autumn is work at school
After the fun summer holidays.

Autumn is Hallowe'en,
When you go round saying, 'Trick or treat'.
Autumn is bonfire night,
Let's drink hot chocolate, yum, yum!

Autumn is leaves falling from trees,
Red, scarlet, purple-coloured leaves.
Autumn is birds,
They go to warmer countries for food like worms. Yuck!

Autumn is weather,
It gets cold, nights longer, days shorter.
Autumn is animals,
Hedgehogs hibernate, so do squirrels!

Autumn is Harvest Festival,
Let's give food to the elderly or poor.
Autumn is to keep warm,
It's very cold, so let's light the fire!

Hannah Breddy (8)
Sandwich Junior School, Sandwich

Fast Cars

F ast cars going *wheeee!*
A lways racing past each other,
S o quick that you cannot see!
T ell your mum and dad and brother.

C an we see them? 'No!' said me.
'A ll I see of them is shadows dear Mother.'
R acing away, they're very scary.
S cary cars went whizzing past.

Bradley Marsh (10)
Sandwich Junior School, Sandwich

My Brother Is . . .

My brother is really annoying
When he keeps on kicking me under the table.
My brother is so smelly,
If you smell my brother you'll die of it.

My brother is such a nerd,
Geek and an idiot.
My brother is rude, nasty
And very rarely good.

My brother is so bad sometimes
I really want to kill him.
My brother is scared of the dark
And sometimes I try to scare him. *(Boo!)*

My brother is really fat, chubby and
If you take off his T-shirt there'll be no room.
My brother is younger than me
And bigger than me.

My brother is also scared
Of being told off by Mum,
But sometimes I take the law into my own hands
And punch him back. *(Oh dear!)*

Harry Sampson (9)
Sandwich Junior School, Sandwich

My Cousin!

My cousin is cool, she's never cruel.
My cousin rides her bike, she loves a hike.
My cousin has a dog, she doesn't go in a pub.
My cousin has a brother, he is not dumb.
My cousin has a mum and dad who are never sad.
My cousin loves animals.
My cousin loves her whole family.

Lisa Harrison (9)
Sandwich Junior School, Sandwich

My Life

When I was one I sucked my thumb.
Mum said stop, because it might go numb.
When I was two I had new shoes.
When I was three I saw the sea
And on that day I sat on a bee.
When I was four I smashed the door,
When I was five I learnt to dive
And drank a drink called Five Alive.
When I was six I went to the Olympics,
When I was seven I saw God in Heaven,
When I was eight I broke my mum's best plate,
When I was nine I wrote a sign,
When I was ten my mum bought a hen,
When I was eleven my dad went to Heaven.

William Bedford (9)
Sandwich Junior School, Sandwich

Through My Life

When I was born I ate a thorn,
When I was 1 I was so dumb,
When I was 2 I saw my Aunt Sue,
When I was 3 I saw the sea,
When I was 4 I locked my jaw,
When I was 5 I choked on a chive,
When I was 6 I ate some sticks,
When I was 7 I prayed in Heaven,
When I was 8 I smashed a plate,
When I was 9 I made Mum's pot shine,
When I was 10 I ate my pen,
When I was 11 my cousin was 7.

John Sandy-Hindmarch (9)
Sandwich Junior School, Sandwich

Autumn Is . . .

Autumn is cold, wet and dark,
Morning cold and dark frost on windows.

Autumn is giving food to old and poor,
Marshmallows cooking on the bonfire.

Autumn is hedgehogs hibernating
And squirrels looking for nuts.

Autumn is going back to school
And new work.

Autumn is leaves, gold and scarlet red.
Flowers die and trees empty.

Autumn is hot chocolate,
Toffee apples and apple and blackberry pie.

Erin Gilham (9)
Sandwich Junior School, Sandwich

My Brother

My brother is the best,
Even though he is a pest.
He always makes me laugh, tee, hee, hee,
And that's why he's the best to me.

He always laughs at me when Man U lose,
But at least I can tie my shoes.
He picks on me when Arsenal win,
But I'll pop his laughter with a pin.

He always beats me on the PlayStation,
But he got lost at a train station.
I always beat him at football
And that's why I totally rule!

Jordan Maclaurin (9)
Sandwich Junior School, Sandwich

Autumn Is

Autumn is conkers - glossy, gleaming, polished, pearly,
smooth as silk, they conquer the conkers.

Autumn is harvest with the wheat shimmering and glistening in the sun
and the apples in shades of sour green and rosy red.

Autumn is hibernation, the squirrels gathering their nuts
and the badgers nestling in their setts.

Autumn is migration, the birds stand drawn up tall just like soldiers,
gathering on the telephone wires.

Autumn is leaves sweeping down in shades of a crisp brown
and a mustard yellow and a dull but lovely orange crunch
under my feet, rustling in the wind.

Autumn is Hallowe'en, cackling witches and pillowcase ghosts.
Luxury, bright, seedy pumpkins, sweets are what it's all about,
stuffing your face till you're horribly sick all over Mum and Dad.

Elizabeth Stowell (8)
Sandwich Junior School, Sandwich

Autumn Is . . .

Autumn is conkers, all shiny and shimmery and brown
                                        with a spiky shell.
Autumn is hibernation, when the animals hide away.
Autumn is migration, when the birds fly south.
Autumn is leaves, brown, orange and red.
Autumn is Hallowe'en, when the ghosts come out to haunt you.
Autumn is harvest, with loads of juicy fruits, and corn is lovely too.
Autumn is morning dew, all glistening and white like diamonds,
Carelessly cast across an emerald carpet.

Matilda Scott-Neve (8)
Sandwich Junior School, Sandwich

What I Like About My Aunties And Uncles

What I like about my aunties and uncles is
they give me presents that are brilliant.

What I like about my aunties and uncles is
they come round to see us every weekend
and stay for tea.

What I like about my aunties and uncles is
they set practical jokes on me that are brilliant,
but I do it better!

What I like about my aunties and uncles is
they let me play with their pets
and my cousins play with them too.

What I like about my aunties and uncles is
they help out with the family and they care for us.

What I like about my aunties and uncles is
they have a big house and a big garden.

But most of all, I love them!

Helen Jarvis (9)
Sandwich Junior School, Sandwich

Autumn Is . . .

Autumn is when leaves fall off the oak trees.
Autumn is when leaves fall off trees, gold, red, yellow, brown, orange.
Autumn is when the night turns cold and dark.
Autumn is when animals go out for food.
Autumn is when we celebrate the 31st of October.
Autumn is when you eat and stay up late on bonfire night.
Autumn is when you cook roast chicken.
Autumn is when Mum bakes pies.

Gareth Williams (8)
Sandwich Junior School, Sandwich

Autumn Is . . .

Autumn is leaves falling down and children
Jumping in heaps of brown and crispy leaves.
Autumn is animals finding food for their warmth to hibernate
And birds flying in the high sky to get to warm countries.

Autumn is children going to school,
Getting new teachers and going into new classes.
Autumn is when the weather is getting colder,
And days getting shorter and nights getting longer.

Autumn is Hallowe'en where you cut out a pumpkin
To make into a candle or yummy, slimy soup.
Autumn is bonfire night on 5th of November,
Having lovely warm, hot chocolate and jacket potatoes
With different fillings inside.

Harriet Jackson (8)
Sandwich Junior School, Sandwich

When I Was Born

When I was born I sat on a thorn,
When I was one, I had just begun,
When I was two I was almost new,
When I was three I sat on a bee,
When I was four I ran into a door,
When I was five, I ate a chive,
When I was six I began to fix,
When I was seven I believed in Heaven,
When I was eight I had a mate,
Now I am nine I stand out and shine!

Kirstie Carless (9)
Sandwich Junior School, Sandwich

Autumn Is . . .

Autumn is cold and wet,
Lots of leaves falling off the trees.

Autumn is shorter days
And longer nights.

Autumn is giving food
To the poor and old.

Autumn is finding acorns
On the ground.

Autumn is cooking potatoes
On the bonfire.

Autumn is squirrels
Hibernating in warm places.

Autumn is grass dew
Every morning.

Jade Mosley (8)
Sandwich Junior School, Sandwich

Autumn Is . . .

Autumn is days getting shorter and nights getting longer.
Autumn is squirrels, hedgehogs, foxes and badgers
Hunting for food.
Autumn is leaves falling down, shades of brown
Scarlet, red, yellow and purple.
Autumn is warm beds and snuggly toys,
Not to forget a nice hug.
Autumn is apple and blackberry pie,
Hot chocolate and toffee apples.

Charlotte Kenton (8)
Sandwich Junior School, Sandwich

Autumn Is . . .

Autumn is the time when the weather is sad
And when the leaves start falling.
Autumn is when birds look for food
And creatures hibernate till spring.

Autumn is Hallowe'en when
Witches and wizards knock on the door.
Autumn is when we give food
To the poor in the town.

Autumn is bonfire night
And the fireworks light up the night sky.
Autumn is cold nights, warm clothes,
Scarf, hat and boots.

Joshua Relton (8)
Sandwich Junior School, Sandwich

Autumn Is . . .

Autumn is when crispy brown leaves fall off the trees.
Autumn is when flowers start to die.

Autumn is when we eat toffee apples.
Autumn is when we eat apple and blackberry pie.

Autumn is when the days get shorter.
Autumn is when the nights get longer.

Autumn is when we make pumpkin candles.
Autumn is when we say, 'Trick or treat'.

Autumn is when we drink hot chocolate.
Autumn is when we eat jacket potatoes.

William Mellin (8)
Sandwich Junior School, Sandwich

Autumn Is

Autumn is conkers, glossy, gleaming, polished, pearly,
smooth as silk, conquerors of other conkers.
Autumn is harvest, rice, wheat, corn, apples, blackberries,
combine harvester roaring through the fields.
Autumn is hibernation, birds flying south, flying in flocks,
flying away from the cold to the warm.
Autumn is migration, birds on the telegraph wires getting ready
for their big journey south away from coldness.
Autumn is leaves, gold, red, brown floating down off the tree
and on the ground, the crunching leaves on the ground go
crunch, crunch.
Autumn is morning dew, throws water across the world making
it freezing cold.
Autumn is Hallowe'en, where you go round people's houses
saying trick or treat and getting sweets and eating them
until you're sick.

Andrew Kirby (8)
Sandwich Junior School, Sandwich

Autumn Is . . .

Autumn is getting darker and summer is fading in the past.
Leaves start to fall off trees.
Autumn is the time when creatures start to hibernate.
Autumn stays for three months.
Autumn is cold and soggy
With dark clouds floating over you like a shadow
But sometimes there's sunshine.
Autumn is close to Hallowe'en with trick or treating.

Matthew Sharman (8)
Sandwich Junior School, Sandwich

Water

Home giver,
Gloom feeder,
Cold giver,
Misery maker,
Thirst taker,
Fire killer,
People drowner,
Great swimmer,
Plate cleaner,
Pipe washer,
Habitat killer,
Sand sweeper,
Cleanliness keeper,
Humans weeper,
Hypothermia bringer,
Happiness taker.

William French (10)
Sandwich Junior School, Sandwich

Water Kennings

Fire quencher,
River flower,
Human drencher,
Flower grower,
Fish helper,
Child killer,
Coral liver,
Ice maker,
Salt eater,
Rock smasher,
Hand scolder,
Cold bringer.

Marc Young (10)
Sandwich Junior School, Sandwich

Water Kennings

Fire fighter,
Ice maker
Frost biter,
Great refresher,
Plant grower,
Heat hater,
Life killer,
Heart breaker,
Hand scolder,
Cold bringer,
Sea lapper,
Live saver,
Plant feeder,
Sand taker,
Rain giver,
Clothes cleaner.

Natasha Westwood (10)
Sandwich Junior School, Sandwich

Fire Kennings

Air gobbler,
Building burner,
Water fighter,
Finger scolder,
Candle lighter,
Hair singer,
Lip prickler,
Hand warmer,
Sweat maker,
Children frightner,
Shock maker,
Heart breaker,
Chill giver.

Naomi Ward (10)
Sandwich Junior School, Sandwich

Air

Hurricane maker,
Wind chime shaker,
Hairdryer charger,
Bubble enlarger,
Sound carrier,
Gas barrier,
Life bringer,
Bell ringer,
Tree uprooter,
Leaf looter,
Kite flyer,
Clothes dryer,
Balloon filler,
Drink spiller,
Sky ruler,
Skin cooler.

Joe Wheeler (10)
Sandwich Junior School, Sandwich

Air Kennings

Life saver,
Recorder blower,
Leaf blower,
Kite flyer,
Whistle blower,
Fire spreader,
Earth lover,
Cloud mover,
Hurricane maker,
Dust bringer,
Sun lover,
Tree mover,
T-shirt blower,
Dart hardener,
Ground blower.

Jade Gothard (10)
Sandwich Junior School, Sandwich

Fire Kennings

Body warmer,
Leaf grower,
Water hater,
Child player,
House brightener,
Wood burner,
Air polluter,
Animal hater,
Heart healer,
Ice melter,
Skin burner,
Food grower,
Bird lover,
House burner,
Cloud shaker,
Flower waker.

Jordan Green (10)
Sandwich Junior School, Sandwich

Water Kennings

Human refresher,
Big cleaner,
Skin wrinkler,
Fire fighter,
House flooder,
Plant grower,
Rock destroyer,
Ice maker,
Cold giver,
Electric danger,
Pen smudger,
Paper ripper,
Heat stopper,
Surf giver.

Jack Barber (10)
Sandwich Junior School, Sandwich

Autumn Is . . .

Autumn is when flowers start dying,
The trees lose their leaves.
Autumn is when it starts to get cold,
Frosty mornings and dew on the grass.

Autumn is when animals start to hibernate,
The squirrels collecting nuts.
Autumn is when the birds fly south,
Hedgehogs under bushes.

Autumn is when we eat and drink,
Jacket potatoes and hot chocolate.
Autumn is when we eat apple and blackberry pie,
We drink hot blackcurrant.

Daisy Kemp (8)
Sandwich Junior School, Sandwich

Fire

(Kennings Style)

Rain scarer,
Heat maker,
Hay burner,
Food heater,
Corn grower,
Lantern feeder,
House destroyer,
Smoke bringer,
Bulb seeder,
Plant weeder,
Heartbroken screamer,
Vision dreamer.

Benjamin Cockram (10)
Sandwich Junior School, Sandwich

Water

Cool refresher,
Flower feeder,
Fire basher,
Thirst smasher,
People drowner,
Ripple maker,
Ever liver,
Constant giver,
Car washer,
Grass feeder,
Tap giver,
Instant liver,
Sea freezer,
Ice maker,
Tongue taster,
Sweat taker.

Robert Kirby (10)
Sandwich Junior School, Sandwich

Fire Kennings

Doom seeker,
Water hater,
People killer,
House burner,
Skin wrinkler,
Paper destroyer,
Heart breaker,
Rocket racer.

Michael Jarrett (10)
Sandwich Junior School, Sandwich

Different People

There are people big and small,
Short and tall, shy and hairy,
Brave, also scary. Some are
Chubby and flubby, large or scruffy.

All people are different midgets,
Always fight like giants have their own clients.
Some have big heads, some small,
Some shaped as a football.

Many have rough skin, smooth skin, flat skin,
Tanned skin. Blond hair, brown hair,
Ginger hair and red hair.
Hair on us and hair on a bear.

People have different imaginations,
Some think of flying sheep and pigs,
Others might think of
Frogs and fierce hogs.

Different people, different legs,
Hairy legs, smooth legs, long legs,
Short legs, fat legs and thin legs,
And some have pig legs.

Kids are people too,
Kids like having fun
Laying in the sun,
Being bad, sitting.

Rebecca Chamberlain (10)
Sandwich Junior School, Sandwich

Small Kids

Small kids are really good,
But big kids are bad.
Small kids wear a hood,
Because big kids are mad.

Small kids are really scared,
But big kids are really cool.
Small kids never get dared
But big kids think they're really tall.

Small kids are no way bossy,
They never know it all,
But big girls are always glossy,
And small kids don't go to the mall.

Small kids are never rude,
Big kids are always in a mood,
Small kids might sometimes be crude,
But big girls think they're a dude.

Small kids don't chat in class,
Big kids break the glass.
Small kids are never daft,
Big kids never laugh.

Small kids obey things,
Big kids are always a pest.
Small kids always wear rings
And big kids don't wear a vest.

Hannah Knowler (10)
Sandwich Junior School, Sandwich

Water

Life reviver,
Thirst killer,
Plant feeder,
Food maker,
Flood bringer,
Whirl pooler,
Ship killer,
Life ender,
Warm bather,
People washer,
Soap dissolver,
Germ killer,
Pool filler,
Fun swimmer,
Chlorine holder,
Eye burner.

Vivienne Hayles (11)
Sandwich Junior School, Sandwich

Autumn Is . . .

Autumn is cold and frosty
And animals start to hibernate.
Autumn is a time when birds go to hot countries,
The days get longer and colder.
Warm coats are out for sale.
Autumn is when the nights get longer.
Autumn is a time when we all wrap up warm.
Autumn is when Hallowe'en comes and we dress up old and scary.
We go back to school and we get a new teacher.

Hannah Trew (8)
Sandwich Junior School, Sandwich

Autumn Is!

Autumn is frosty and wet
Leaves fall from the trees and birds are going away.

Autumn is animals hibernating
Squirrels collecting nuts for the long winter.

Autumn is Hallowe'en
When we knock on doors and say trick or treat.

Autumn is Bonfire Night
Where we remember Guy Fawkes.

Autumn is going back to school
And having a new teacher.

Autumn is weather
Getting colder and the days are shorter.

Autumn is trees
Leaves, crispy brown and yellow.

Charlye Hodgkins-Hale (8)
Sandwich Junior School, Sandwich

Fire Kennings

Street burner,
Heart warmer,
Skin burner,
Greatest icebreaker,
Skin wrinkler,
Blonde maker,
Soul shaker.

Holly Groombridge (10)
Sandwich Junior School, Sandwich

Animal Poems

M ousey Mouse is so sweet
O h just look at his tiny feet
U gly is what a mouse can't be
S o mice are great according to me
E verybody loves Mousey Mouse.

R avens are black
A nd have purple eyes
V ery big is what they are
E very raven is very fast
N ot very many people like ravens.

O ctopus is wiggly
C olour change is what they can do
T hey can squirt ink
O ctopus has lots of different colours
P urple, red, green, blue and lots more
U nder the sand is where they hide
S ometimes they attack, sometimes they are friendly.

D ogs are big and small
O r they are different colours
G etting a dog is exciting.

W olves howl at the moon
O n mountains
L ots of wolves go around in a 'pack'
F ur is very long on a wolf to keep it warm.

Rosie Charter (10)
Sandwich Junior School, Sandwich

My Nasty Brother

My brother always says to me, 'Please leave some for me.'
My dad is always grumpy because my brothers are silly.
My niece is always important to me,
But when she died I felt so sad and upset.
I am always the last to go to wash my hair in the bath tub.

Becky Brisley (9)
Sandwich Junior School, Sandwich

What My Sister Has Done For Me

When I was born she held me, she hugged me,
She cuddled me when I was sad,
Played with me when I was down,
Calmed me when I was mad.

She pushed me in my pram,
And fed me when I was hungry,
She helped me to walk and stand up straight,
And helped me when I was tumbly.

When I got older she did my hair,
She looked after me when my mom wasn't there,
And took me on the rides in the fair,
I trusted her so I did not fear.

Now she bosses me around sometimes,
But I think of all the things she has done for me,
I do really love my sister,
And she loves me.

Abigail Greenfield (9)
Sandwich Junior School, Sandwich

Growing Up

When I was one I had a smelly bum,
When I was two I learnt to chew,
When I was three I bounced on my mum's knee,
When I was four I learnt to draw,
When I was five I wanted to drive,
When I was six I had three Weetabix,
When I was seven I saw my Uncle Kevin.

Tom Rigden (9)
Sandwich Junior School, Sandwich

Moany Mum

Mum, moany Mum,
Do this, do that,
Don't forget to brush your teeth,
Give me a kiss, don't tell lies.
Oh my moany mum!

Mum, moany Mum,
Take the rabbit out of the run,
Clean out the hamster,
Take the dog for a walk,
Oh my moany mum!

Mum, moany Mum,
Tidy your room, tidy the shed,
Water the plants, do your chores,
Mow the lawn, cuddle Pippin,
Oh my moany mum!

Mum, moany Mum,
Vacuum the carpet, wash the windows,
Dust the ornaments, wash the car,
Do the dishes, fold the washing,
Oh my moany mum!

Mum, my mum,
Sure she moans and groans at me,
But I still love her and she loves me.
She feeds me and cuddles me
And kisses me goodnight,
I suppose she's not that bad,
Not my mum!

Chloé Forsyth (9)
Sandwich Junior School, Sandwich

Music

Music, for me, is fantastic and fun,
Though it is a lesson, so work must be done.
The crotchets, the quavers, the minims too,
All put together, they make a tune.
Practice makes perfect, so soon it sounds great,
Apart from the scales which I really hate.
My teacher is always cheerful and happy,
She likes all music that is snappy.
I like my lessons, so I'm never late,
I hope one day I'll be Grade 8.
If you listen and hear a sound,
You'll hear music, it's all around.
When I walk down my street,
Music comes beneath my feet.
Concerts and festivals are a wow,
Live without music, I don't know how.
Music speaks in many different tongues,
Rock guitars and African drums.
Singing at sleepovers, dancing all night,
Hearing through headphones the music I like.
Music lifts my spirits high,
Music makes my soul heave a sigh.
Music is everywhere, all different types,
Even in the mountains where people hike.
Loud or soft, slow or fast,
I like music, so long as it lasts.
Christmas time means music galore,
Carols are pretty, but church is a bore.
I prefer carolling with my friends,
Singing songs 'til Christmas ends.

Lauren Maw (10)
Sandwich Junior School, Sandwich

Water

Thirst quencher,
Misery bringer,
Cold giver,
People drowner,
Throat refresher,
Whirlpool maker,
Car cleaner,
Boat eater,
Bridge breaker,
Fire fighter,
Pain taker,
Healthy drinker,
Pool filler,
Small waver,
Sea saltier,
Much cooler.

Kate Lyden (10)
Sandwich Junior School, Sandwich

Air

Life giver,
Space taker,
Cloud maker,
People breather,
House filler,
Wind blower,
Getting colder,
Gap filler,
Tree blower,
Flower bender,
Dust picker,
Getting slower.

Dan O'Brien (11)
Sandwich Junior School, Sandwich

Fire Kennings

Fast spreader,
Heat giver,
Air eater,
House burner,
Candle lighter,
Great burner,
Hand warmer,
Food cooker,
Night fighter,
Ice melter,
Recent killer,
Attention attractor,
Eye blinder,
Lip prickler,
Heart breaker,
Shock maker.

Dominika Szücsová (10)
Sandwich Junior School, Sandwich

Water Kennings

Plant drinker,
Body water,
Wet river,
Sea lover,
Bath washer,
Mud cleaner,
Hair washer,
Hair cleaner,
Drink refresher.

Chelsea Cox (10)
Sandwich Junior School, Sandwich

All About Me And My Fave Things

My name is Samantha,
I like the Pink Panther,
I am 10 years of age,
And I have one brother
And three sisters.
I have a big family.
I go to Sandwich Junior School.
When I am older
I want to be in the police force.
My hobby is tidying and sorting things out.
While I have been at Sandwich Junior School
I have been in classes 3CR, 4L, 5B and 6H.
My fave video is 'Josie And The Pussy Cats'
And my fave book is 'Girl In Love'.
So far I have enjoyed my new class.
My fave dinner is pasta.

Samantha Martin (10)
Sandwich Junior School, Sandwich

My Family

My family can be happy,
My family can be sad,
My family can be good
And my family can be bad.
My family can be helpful
And often very kind,
Sometimes they see clearly
And sometimes they are blind.
But always they are there for me
To guide me on my way,
They are the thing that doesn't change
For me in my average, normal day.

Rosie Beale (9)
Sandwich Junior School, Sandwich

What My Sister Has Done For Me

She pushed me in my pram,
And fed me when I was hungry,
Calmed me down when I was mad,
Cuddled me when I was sad.
She cared and looked after me when my mum wasn't there,
Played with me when I was down.
When I was born she held and stroked me,
She taught me to walk,
And hugged me at the end.
Read stories and sung nursery rhymes to make me sleep,
And helped me to speak.
She let me join in with her homework,
And helped me with mine.

Now she bosses me about most times,
But I think of all the things she has done for me,
I really do love my sister.

Ellen Hall (9)
Sandwich Junior School, Sandwich

Autumn Is!

Autumn is when animals hibernate and the leaves fall off trees,
Autumn is when people pack up for winter and go somewhere warm.
Autumn is when you put summer clothes in your drawer
and get autumn clothes.
Autumn is when squirrels are looking for food
and birds are looking for food too.
Autumn is when big, thick, grey clouds appear
and the stars fill up the sky,
Autumn is when you have Hallowe'en and you can go trick or treating.
Autumn is when Guy Fawkes blows up the Houses of Parliament
and you have fireworks.
Autumn is when conkers fall from a horse chestnut tree.
Autumn is when nights get longer and days get shorter.

Bethany Gibson (8)
Sandwich Junior School, Sandwich

Big Kids

Big kids are bossy,
They think they know it all.
Big girls are glossy,
And big boys play pool.

Big kids can be nice,
When you're not a pest.
The girls are scared of mice,
While the boys think they're the best.

Big kids are mean,
And little kids are kind.
Big kids like Mr Bean,
But little kids don't mind.

Big kids are really bad,
But little kids are really good.
Big kids get very mad
And little kids wear hoods.

Big kids are really tall
And little kids are really short.
Big kids go to the mall,
While little kids go snort, snort, snort.

Big kids are really naughty,
Like big kids chat in class.
Big boys say they're forty,
Big girls break the glass.

Rachel Collins (10)
Sandwich Junior School, Sandwich

Autumn Is

Autumn is: Apples, ripe and juicy, fresh farm produce
to sink your teeth into.
Autumn is: Conkers, glossy, gleaming, polished, pearly,
smooth as silk, conquering other conkers.

Megan Reeve (8)
Sandwich Junior School, Sandwich

Autumn Is

Autumn is conkers falling from the trees
brown, shiny conkers in their shells
Autumn is back to school with new teachers and classes
you might even have a new school,

Autumn is colder days, shorter days
but longer nights
Autumn is harvest festival,
giving food for the elderly.

Autumn is Hallowe'en
knocking on doors shouting *trick or treat!*
Autumn is fireworks
shooting up into the sky.

Autumn is Bonfire Night
on the 5th November
Autumn is toffee apples and jacket potatoes
maybe even blackberry pie, yum!

Autumn is flowers
that are dying
Autumn is leaves
falling on the dewy grass.

Autumn is birds flying away
to warmer countries
Autumn is animals
doing their hibernation.

Fraser Meldrum (8)
Sandwich Junior School, Sandwich

Autumn Is

Autumn is changing weather, cold and windy.
Autumn, wear warm clothes and wellie boots.
Autumn is squirrels and hedgehogs.
Autumn is leaves falling off the trees.

Sophie Kennett (8)
Sandwich Junior School, Sandwich

Water Kennings

Fire destroyer,
Plant grower,
Heat hater,
Life killer,
Ice melter,
Life saver,
Fish helper,
Ice maker,
Wave maker,
Shell shaker,
Wave hitter,
Soft toucher,
Hand scolder,
Clothes washer,
Cold bringer,
Sea leaper.

Elliot Torbett (10)
Sandwich Junior School, Sandwich

Fire Kennings

Plant shrinker,
Hazard maker,
Flame breather,
Smoke sizzler,
Ground killer,
House burner,
Sweat maker,
Cloud shaker.

David Buckmaster (10)
Sandwich Junior School, Sandwich

Water

Thirst quencher,
Clothes drencher,
Whirlpool maker,
Fire killer,
Plant grower,
Ice maker,
Life saver,
Life taker,
Lake sweller,
Raindrop maker,
Cold keeper,
Sea leaper,
Rock breaker,
Sand taker,
River flower,
Hand scolder.

Gabrielle Quinn (10)
Sandwich Junior School, Sandwich

Water Kennings

Mud cleaner,
Mighty destroyer,
Living master,
Shore lover,
Rubbish scatterer,
Fire hater,
Ship wrecker,
Big hugger.

Sam Bean (10)
Sandwich Junior School, Sandwich

Autumn Is!

Autumn is leaves and conkers
Falling to the ground
Autumn is when the flowers start to die
And the animals hibernate.

Autumn is when frost falls to the ground
Rabbits and foals roam around
Autumn is cold and dark
And summer has passed.

Autumn is when houses are lit up
And the radiators are on
Autumn is when we have
Hot jacket potatoes in the oven.

Autumn is when we give
Food to the poor and elderly
Autumn is when we have
Harvest festivals.

Autumn is when we go back
To school and more work
Autumn is when you have a new teacher
And a new class.

Autumn is when hedgehogs
And squirrels start to hibernate
Autumn is when the animals are gathering
Food for the winter.

Hannah Taylor (8)
Sandwich Junior School, Sandwich

Autumn Is!

Autumn is when the earth gets colder
And when people gather around the fire
Autumn is when animals gather good and start to hibernate.

Autumn is when leaves change colour
And drop down from the trees.
Autumn is when children climb chestnut trees
And collect all of the conkers.

Autumn is when the weather gets colder
And the frost starts to form.
Autumn is when the days get shorter
And the nights grow longer.

Autumn is when the birds start to fly south
Where the climate is warmer.
Autumn is when we start to celebrate
And when we cook jacket potatoes on a bonfire.

Autumn is when it's Hallowe'en
And people trick or treat.
Autumn is when we have bonfires
And noisy fireworks up in the sky.

Autumn is when we invite families and friends
To eat apple pie, mmm!
Autumn is when we give food to the poor
And celebrate harvest time.

Brennan Westwood (8)
Sandwich Junior School, Sandwich

Autumn Is

Autumn is crispy, it has conkers as smooth as silk.
Autumn is a time when the leaves fall off the trees.
Autumn is a time when you just wake up and look out of the window
and see morning dew.
Autumn is when farmers have harvest, when they get their food.
Autumn is when the apples glow ruby, the pears glow emerald,
the blackberries gleam like jewels.
Autumn is when Hallowe'en comes, when we believe that spirits
come out to visit us, when we also dress up in scary costumes.

Georgia Down (8)
Sandwich Junior School, Sandwich

Fire Kennings

Burner maker,
Hotter warmer,
Doom-seeker lighter,
House burner,
Colour fuller,
Browner flamer,
Burning heartbreaker.

Stacey Cornwall (10)
Sandwich Junior School, Sandwich

Fire Kennings

Smoke bringer,
Hatred singer,
Plant killer,
Sadness leader,
Gas breather,
Heart breaker,
Soul shaker,
Environment taker.

Laura Roscoe (10)
Sandwich Junior School, Sandwich

Autumn Is

Autumn is: Conkers, glossy, gleaming, polished, pearly,
smooth as silk, conquering other conkers.
Autumn is: Harvest with harvest cutting tonnes of delicious hazelnuts,
berries, pears, apples from the trees, the apples so juicy it is like
I'm in a lake.
Autumn is: Hibernation when the badgers go to sleep in their holes
in the ground.
Autumn is: Hallowe'en, when you go round houses in scary costumes
saying trick or teat and people give you sweets and money.

Simon Malhomme (8)
Sandwich Junior School, Sandwich

Autumn Is!

Autumn is Bonfire Night, and the fire's alight
Autumn is toffee apple, nice and crisp
Autumn is fireworks whizzing in the dark sky
Autumn is sparklers sparkling in the night
Autumn is little men running around with matches and lighters
Autumn is Hallowe'en witches, wizards and pumpkins
Autumn is when the leaves fall off the trees
Autumn is when men cut wood for the fire.

Jacob Burslem (8)
Sandwich Junior School, Sandwich

Water

Body washer,
Plant helper,
Rain giver,
Wet maker,
River flower,
Dancing flower,
Common speaker,
Whirlpool maker.

Emily Harris (10)
Sandwich Junior School, Sandwich

A Cat In A Rap World

The cat who lives down the lane
Yesterday fell down the drain,
'Miaow, miaow,' he said,
Which means am I dead?

He then awoke from a deep nap,
And ran out the house through his cat flap,
He found a tree which he jumped up and rolled in a ball,
Zzzzzz . . .

One hour later,
He heard pitter-patter,
It was raining dogs, but not cats,
Then the cat from down the lane
Fell out of the tree, what a shame!
He ran back inside where it was nice and dry,
But he sat on the frying pan and fried.

2 hours later,
He was in a vet's,
With lots of other ill pets,
In a cage next to him was a bulldog,
But the cat thought it was a bullfrog.

So the cat said,
'Here boy, are you dead?'
'Woof, woof,' said the dog,
The cat sank like he was in a bog.

Soon the cat was back at home,
He saw the bulldog on a phone,
Ring, ring, the phone went, the cat answered it,
'Come outside,' the dog said, so the cat did,
'Woof, woof, miaow, miaow,' said the cat. 'Boy I'm a twit!'

Christopher Arman (10)
Sandwich Junior School, Sandwich

My Hobbies

B allet is fun for me
A twizzle and a sauté
L ook at me, I'm in a ballet show
L eaping gracefully into the air
E veryone you meet is friendly
T wizzles are good fun as well.

B allet keeps you fit
A lways great fun
L ovely third position, Abigail
L anding softly on the ground
E xpressing my expression
T wirl and a flip.

B allet is my hobby
A n elephant noise is wrong
L ittle giggle, little laugh
L ook at me with my ballet shoes on
E nding a performance with a . . .
T wirl.

B allet makes your posture straight
A ballet show gives me nerves
L a, la, la goes the music
L a, la, la
E ntering the doors of the ballet class
T aking a bow at the end.

B arre work is fun
A plié makes a diamond in your knees
L ovely transfer of weight
L ight pink cosies
E nter the stage for a show with a smile
T urn around on your tiptoes.

Abigail Harrop (10)
Sandwich Junior School, Sandwich

Autumn Is

Autumn is conkers, glossy, gleaming, polished, pearly,
smooth as silk, conkers of other conkers.
Autumn is hibernating, when squirrels hibernate in their lovely,
warm, snug home.
Autumn is morning dew like glittering crystals glinting in the sun.
Autumn is Hallowe'en when people go out in the pitch-black night,
going trick or treating and ringing on people's doors.
Autumn is when birds migrate to fly to the south.
Autumn is rosy red apples and pears have a glow of green
and cornfields and berries as red as blood.
Autumn is when the leaves go gold, red, russet, brown
and when you walk the leaves go crunch, crunch, crunch.

Shafaye Abbot (8)
Sandwich Junior School, Sandwich

Autumn Is!

Autumn is when the animals hibernate
It is cold and frosty.

Autumn is having Bonfire Night
And hot jacket potatoes.

Autumn is splashing around in the puddles.

Autumn is when the days get shorter
And the nights get longer.

Harry Lawrence (8)
Sandwich Junior School, Sandwich

Autumn Is

Brown falling leaves in the month.
Conkers going down from the conker trees.
Autumn is Hallowe'en with evil faces that gloom.

Heather Godfrey (8)
Sandwich Junior School, Sandwich

Autumn Is

Autumn is: Conkers, glossy, gleaming, polished, pearly,
smooth as silk, conquerors of other conkers.

Autumn is: harvest where you give food to people
if they have not got any food like in Africa.

Autumn is: Hallowe'en where you do trick and treat,
it's where you go and knock on people's doors and you ask
if you can have some sweets, sometimes they don't want
to have people knocking at their houses.

Autumn is: Hibernation, badgers, squirrels, frogs lie snug
and safe, they're silent and sleeping.

Ryan Tench (8)
Sandwich Junior School, Sandwich

Autumn Is

Autumn is conkers, glossy, gleaming, polished, pearly,
Smooth as silk, conquerors of other conkers.

Autumn is when apples are ripe and juicy,
They're growing on a tree with blackberries and other fruit.

Autumn is when tortoises go to sleep and badgers go to their setts
And go to sleep maybe for a year.

Lauren Beale (8)
Sandwich Junior School, Sandwich

Growing Up Poem

When I was one I sucked my thumb
When I was two I went to the zoo
When I was three I swam in the sea
When I was four my leg was sore
When I was five I nearly died
When I was six I picked up some sticks
When I was seven I went to Devon.

Dominic Pettit (9)
Sandwich Junior School, Sandwich

Me!

Now this is a poem all about me, now would you listen carefully
When I was 1 I sucked my thumb
When I was 2 I went on a cruise
When I was 3 I climbed a tree
When I was 4 I broke the law
When I was 5 I sat on a beehive
When I was 6 I ate a Twix
When I was 7 I went to Heaven
When I was 8 I broke a plate
When I was 9 I broke a vine
When I was 10 I saw a hen
When I was 11 I came back home.

Jack Brown (9)
Sandwich Junior School, Sandwich

Autumn Is!

Autumn is when it is wet, frosty and getting darker
The days are getting shorter and nights longer
Autumn is animals starting to hibernate and look for food.

Autumn is Hallowe'en, witches and wizards
Knock on the door and trick or treat
Autumn is going back to school
Where we meet different teachers and go to new classes.

Autumn is Bonfire Night on 5th of November
With fireworks in the sky and sparklers in the air
Autumn is toffee apples with apple and blackberry pie.

Robert Holbrook (8)
Sandwich Junior School, Sandwich

My Family

My brother's room is like a forest
There's trees and fleas
With birds everywhere.

My sister's room is like a Barbie house
It's got fairy lights
And Barbie dolls everywhere.

My brother's room is like an ocean
With fishes, dishes and lots of kisses
And whales with his scales.

My mum's room is like a desert
With spiders and snakes everywhere
There's sand blowing in your faces.

My dad's room is like a football pitch
He always shouts, 'Goal!'

Ben Skirrow (9)
Sandwich Junior School, Sandwich

Tidy Your Room

My brother's room is like a jungle
I can see parrots, cheetahs, snakes and apes
My brother's room is like an ocean
Whales and ripped boat sails.

My sister's room is like a Barbie house
There's fairy eyes and smelly flies
My sister's room is like a forest
She says she can hear funny cries but of course she always lies.

Tidy your room my mum says, but it's tidy.

Peter Turay (9)
Sandwich Junior School, Sandwich

A School Morning

I'm sleeping in my bed,
With my covers on my head,
I'm having a great dream,
Then I hear my mum scream,
'Get up, it's time for school!'

So I got out of bed,
Just like my mum said,
I slouched down the hall,
Then I heard my mum call,
'Don't forget to brush your teeth!'

I ate my breakfast quick,
Then I heard the clock go tick,
Time was running out,
Then I heard my mum shout,
'Get yourself out of the door child!'

Rebecca Sullivan (9)
Sandwich Junior School, Sandwich

My Brother Harry

When I was little Harry pushed me off the highchair
When I was little Harry pulled me down the stairs
When I was little Harry ruined my painting

When I was little Harry always drank my juice
When I was little Harry almost killed me
When I was little Harry made me choke

When I was little Harry tried to stick a nail in my head
When I was little Harry always annoyed me
When I was little Harry . . . ruined my *life!*

Charlie Skinner (9)
Sandwich Junior School, Sandwich

My Sister Jane

I have a sister,
Her name is Jane.
Jane's a real pain,
A pain in the neck.

My older sister
Always beats me at Twister.
Jane's a real drain,
And a pain in the neck.

She's older than me,
And I have to flee.
Jane's a real meanie,
And a pain in the neck.

Jane goes, 'Snore, snore, snore,'
She's a gigantic bore.
Jane's a real pain,
A pain in the neck.

Lydia Sinnett-Smith   (9)
Sandwich Junior School, Sandwich

When I Was One

When I was one I used my potty
When I was two I broke my thumb
When I was three I ate my socks
When I was four I could kick a ball
When I was five I climbed the tree and broke my arm
When I was six I found a plum and threw it at my mum
When I was seven I kicked my dad
When I was eight he kicked me back
When I was nine I was fast asleep.

Ryan Brown   (9)
Sandwich Junior School, Sandwich

Sport

F ootball is a world famous sport,
O h no, what a goal by Ronaldo,
O h no, Liverpool have got a penalty,
T hierry Henry, what a player!
B rilliant ball control, look at him go,
A scorcher of a goal by Rooney for United,
L osers Liverpool, unlucky, ha ha,
L ast minute there goes the whistle, 2-1 to United.

C aught out for 0, unlucky,
R ubbish umpire, I think he's blind,
I can't believe it, we've won , we've beaten Australia,
C ricket, one of the best sports around,
K ent, second in the league table,
E ngland, England, England, England, na na,
T reshcothic, the opening batter for England.

Michael Jones (10)
Sandwich Junior School, Sandwich

My Brother And Me

If you want to be my brother
You've got to act normally,
And I might give you money
For something after tea.

It's nice that you're my brother,
If something's up you know what to do,
It's something you really should do,
Because I would come to you.

But my anger gets really bad,
So sometimes I go to Mum,
But you're my brother all the same,
I'm not all that mad.

Eve Batts (9)
Sandwich Junior School, Sandwich

My Family

My brothers, Danny and Darren, always play with me
but sometimes we argue.
When I was one Danny and Darren loved me and cared for me.
When I was two they still cared for me and they played with me.
When I was three I was getting older
and I scored my first goal ever in football.
When I was four my brothers still cared for me
as much as when I was younger.
When I was five my mum and dad split up and married someone else.
When I was six I got more interested in football and I got better.
When I was seven I moved house to Deal and made some new friends.
When I was eight I moved again to Laburnum Avenue
and made more friends.
When I was nine I went on holiday to Spain by a plane.
When I was ten I came back from holiday
and I became more responsible.

Jason Clayton (10)
Sandwich Junior School, Sandwich

When I Was Born

When I was born I couldn't crawl across the lawn,
When I was zero I ate some chocolate Heroes,
When I was one I sucked my thumb,
When I was two I could use the loo,
When I was three I climbed a tree,
When I was four I fell through the floor,
When I was five I learnt to swim and dive,
When I was six I built a house with sticks,
When I was seven I had a holiday in Devon,
When I was eight I ate dinner from a plate,
Now I'm nine and I'm feeling fine.

Jack Butcher (9)
Sandwich Junior School, Sandwich

When I Was Young

When I was young
I wanted a dog
So I could take him for walks in the fog.

When I was young
I wanted a cat
So I could feed him until he was fat.

When I was young
I wanted a gerbil
So I could call him a silly name like Herbil.

When I was young
I wanted a kitten
So I could wrap him up in a little mitten.

When I was young
I wanted a rat
So I could watch him go around and around on a mat.

When I was young
I wanted a snake
So I could scare my uncle Jake.

When I was young
I wanted a mouse
So I could make him a small house.

When I was young
I wanted a bear
So I could give him lots of attention and care.

When I was young
I wanted a duck
So I could mess around in the muck.

When I was older
I got a lizard
And I loved to make her warm
So she didn't think that she was in a blizzard.

Rebecca Reynolds (10)
Sandwich Junior School, Sandwich

Spoilt Rotten

I care for my mum
I care for my dad
I care for my pet
I care for my nan
I care for my aunt
I care for my uncle
I care for my sister
I care for my brother

That's how I get spoilt

I care for my friend Rachel
I care for my friend Hannah
I care for my friend Jessica
I care for my friend Chelsea
I care for my friend Laura
I care for my friend Emily
I care for my friend Melissa

That's how I get spoilt

I care for my teacher Mrs Hutchings
I care for my literacy teacher
I care for my history teacher Mr Allen
I care for my head teacher Mr Rees
I care for my dinner ladies

And that's how I get spoilt

I care for Year 3
I care for Year 4
I care for Year 5
I care for Year 6
And I care for me

And that's how I get spoilt
Isn't it obvious?

Jemma Lowley (10)
Sandwich Junior School, Sandwich

What I Like About My Auntie And Uncle

What I like about my auntie and uncle:
Sometimes they give me sweets,
Sometimes they give me presents for my birthday,
When my mum and dad go out, me and my sister sleep round.
My auntie and uncle have a barbecue, we play games,
My uncle plays good jokes and my sister chuckles.
I play with their pet,
My auntie and uncle's pet is called Bonnie.
Sometimes they come and see us
And sometimes we go and see them,
My auntie and uncle care for us,
My auntie and uncle have a big house and garden
And there is peace for the family!

Jade Beale (9)
Sandwich Junior School, Sandwich

The Best Mum In The World

My mum is the best by far,
She drives a real flash car.
Her hair is long, right down to the ground,
When she moves it swishes around.

She wears black boots and a red cool hat,
A big brown jacket and she's hardly fat.
She wears cool clothes from shops in France,
And always likes to sing and dance.

So we don't need a big protest,
We all know my mum's the best.

Ellie Powling (9)
Sandwich Junior School, Sandwich

My Ages

When I was one I ate a plum,
When I was two I ate my mum's shoe,
When I was three I ate some cheese,
When I was four I kissed a door,
When I was five I learnt to dive,
When I was six I got sticks,
When I was eight I had one mate,
When I was nine I really shined,
When I am ten I will sit on a hen.

Siân Benzies (9)
Sandwich Junior School, Sandwich

Autumn

Leaves are like crashing jet planes,
Trees as bare as a bald man's head,
Rain is a thunderstorm,
Autumn is a leaf bed.

Conkers falling from the trees
And splashing in the puddles,
The air is getting colder,
As the rabbit group huddles.

Children are on leaf piles,
Making crunchy sounds,
Can't be bothered to go to school
Because of the . . .

Amber, brown, yellow and red,
No one wants to get out of bed.
Gold, orange and hazelnut,
Doors and windows have to be shut.

Omid Rajabalipour (10)
South Ascot Village School, Ascot

Everyone Sad

Mums send children to school
Children refuse to go
No one in the pools
Adults fed up
Everyone's sad

Summer equipment all in suitcases
Children kick leaves into piles
Adult late for work
People praying for Christmas
Everyone's sad

Animals collect food for winter
Adults quarrel with each other
Children miserable because of the rain
Babies cry with the wind
Everyone's sad.

Prerna Kapoor (11)
South Ascot Village School, Ascot

Autumn

Twirling, twisting leaves hit the ground,
They hit without making a sound.
Golden leaves flutter to the floor,
Down comes more, more and more.
Autumn is a windy season,
Where trees end up bare.
Amber coloured leaves are on the floor,
Partnered by yellow, gold and red ones.
It starts to rain more often now,
So farmers have to stop the plough.

Liam Kennedy (10)
South Ascot Village School, Ascot

The Autumn Is Like . . .

T he autumn is like a carpet of leaves,
H eavy rain is a sheet of grey,
E verything golden brown.

A utumn leaves are like bronze paper,
U nderneath the litter of orange
T here is little green everywhere,
U nderground the rabbits are preparing for sleep,
M any colours are on the ground,
N o trees anywhere with red leaves on them.

I nside the house we are around the fire
S o we stay warm.

L ittle baby still asleep,
I nterwoven red with the other colours,
K nitted together like a world-wide tapestry.
E verything is autumn.

Nicholas Wiggett (10)
South Ascot Village School, Ascot

Autumn

Autumn is like an attack from planes,
The leaves are kamikazes,
The wind is a screeching phantom
Gliding through the hall,
Whirling, whooshing, windy wind,
Autumn is over,
Winter is coming,
Animals will hibernate and look for food.

Callum Mitchell (10)
South Ascot Village School, Ascot

Autumn

Autumn leaves drop from trees
Whilst conkers drop and bounce like fleas.

The strong wind is blowing
No time for mowing the lawn.

Stay at home and keep warm
Don't go outside, there might be a storm.

Autumn is a colourful time
Gold, brown, orange, red and bronze.

Leaves dying, turning into crust
Conkers rotting, fading away.

Autumn's finished for another day.

Lewis Cornwall (10)
South Ascot Village School, Ascot

Autumn Days

Conkers dive out of the trees
The trees litter the path with leaves
Hurricanes cause loads of terror
Channel 4 news has the weather
Autumn is a load of fun
When the leaves are together
They look like a great big bun
Autumn's like a flock of planes
Even old men snap their canes
People like autumn a lot
But some plants die in their pots
Leaves are dying on the floor
But the trees are giving more and more.

Fraser Morby (10)
South Ascot Village School, Ascot

Autumn

A nimals get ready for winter.
B oys kick leaves at girls.
C ats play with leaves.
D ucks swim up and down.
E ggs have cracked from spring.
F rogs jump, jump, jump.
G rass grows longer.
H ouses light fires.
 I ce cream vans not driving around.
J umbo coats put on.
K icking leaves is fun.
L itter gets blown away.
M ums moan at the coldness.
N uts like conkers fall.
O ak trees have acorns.
P ink wellies slide on feet.
Q uarrels calm down.
R abbits dig holes.
S un fades.
T eachers give homework, children let it blow away.
U mbrellas fly away.
V olcanoes don't burst, the openings are full up with leaves.
W ind swoops past trees.
oX settle down with the herd.
 Y achts float faster with the wind.
 Z ips zip up on coats.

Louella Fox (10)
South Ascot Village School, Ascot

Autumn Things

The trees are like swerving cars.
The leaves are like brown spikes.
The rain is a shining crystal as it falls.
The trees are like twisted tornadoes.
The leaves are floating down from the trees mysteriously.
The children are jumping into the deep piles of leaves.
The parents are angry.

Reece Merryman (10)
South Ascot Village School, Ascot

Autumn Days

Trees sway in the breeze.
They are letting down their leaves,
After a while the children
Jump in all the deep leaves.
It's just an autumn's day
With rain and a carpet of leaves.
The gushing wind howls at the moon,
The leaves hover in the breeze.
It's just an autumn's day
With a carpet of leaves.

Andre Jotle (10)
South Ascot Village School, Ascot

Autumn Day

Gliding leaves gushing in the breeze
Conkers falling from the sky.
Chestnuts hovering in the trees
Gliding, falling, swirling, bang!
The breeze swooping through the trees
Curving, swerving, moaning in the night
Gold leaves falling to the floor.

Christopher Reeves (10)
South Ascot Village School, Ascot

Autumn

Autumn is brown and red,
Autumn is howling wolves,
Autumn is calmness.

Autumn is chocolate,
Autumn is a yellow leather sofa,
Autumn is white wine.

Autumn is an apple orchard,
Autumn is a squirrel.

Mille Roche (10)
South Ascot Village School, Ascot

Autumn Days

The autumn wind blows like howling brown wolves.
Watch the abandoned yellow see-saws
go up and down in the swooping wind,
and under the orange slide
two bronze hedgehogs make a mossy-red leaf house.

Mum's at work taking multicoloured umbrellas out of the rack.
Mumbling children on the school run.
Say goodbye to the sun.

Rebecca Taylor (10)
South Ascot Village School, Ascot

Fear

Fear tastes sour and horrible.
It reminds me of scary Hallowe'en.
The colour is just black, black, black.
The colour is pitch-black scary.
The sound is screaming, screaming.
It's the dark that scares me, screaming.
Fear tastes sour and horrible.

Katie Ray (8)
Stanton Harcourt CE Primary School, Witney

Fear And Silence

Fear is black,
Black as night.
Silence is misty grey,
Misty grey is a mist.
Fear is quiet,
Silence is nothing.
Fear is scary,
Silence is strange.
Fear is sour,
Silence is horrid.
Fear is a horrible movie,
Silence is the best class.

Kyle Luckett (8)
Stanton Harcourt CE Primary School, Witney

My Mum And Dad

My mum and dad are a great pair,
Cos they take us everywhere!
Hope your mums and dads are too,
Cos I think they're the best!

When I was born they cared for me,
Just like a family of birds in a tree.
And even though I'm bigger they still do,
So I think they're the best!

We go to museums and to the park,
And to firework parties after dark.
We always have a lot of fun,
And I think they're the best!

When my friends come round,
Mum and Dad don't make a sound.
Although Mum is a bit bossy!
I still think they're the *best!*

Robert Ford (9)
Stoke Poges Primary School, Slough

My Cat

My cat
Is big and fat
She often lays on the mat
Her name is Pat.

I put her fish
In a dish
It started to rain
We jumped on a train.

There are things my Pat is afraid of like bats
And rats
My Pat likes dressing up in coats
And riding in boats.

Oh Pat my dear
You feel so near
Now listen here
Let's have some beer.

Bethan Nankivell (8)
Stoke Poges Primary School, Slough

My Mum

My mum is sweet,
Because when I'm hungry,
She gives me something to eat.

My mum had three babies,
And when we got home,
My dad got her a Mercedes.

My mum is so lovely,
When I am sad,
She gives me a cuddle.

My mum is the best,
Because she loves
Me and the rest.

Naveen Mahil (7)
Stoke Poges Primary School, Slough

Animals

Animals are wonderful creatures,
They each have their own special features.
Whether it's your pet or out in the wild,
They all bring happiness to every child.
If you want to find out a little bit more,
Please come round my house and knock on the door.
You'll see my rabbit, she's really grumpy,
I'm sure she's a camel cos she's always humpy.
Her name is Snowy because she's white,
You have to be careful in case she'll bite.
Then there's my cat, she's an old lady,
Although that's no excuse for being lazy.
She is very sweet, we call her Coco,
Although some days she's real loco.
Coco sits on the tank and looks at the fish,
Although I'm sure she wants them in her dish.
My favourite is the angelfish with their colours so pretty,
All they want to do is swim in their sea city.
Our neighbour Bernie, who's a very nice man,
Brought some birds home in his van.
I like to sit and watch them, the canaries and the doves,
The zebra finches keep twit-pattering, and falling in love.
Elephants big, mice small,
Hedgehogs that roll up into a ball.
Some fly, some swim,
Some fat, some slim.
Peacocks with their feathers so bright,
Owls that hoot all through the night.
All God's creatures large and small,
Thank You Lord, we love them all.

Lewis Howell (7)
Stoke Poges Primary School, Slough

Camping

At the weekend Mum woke us up early
And told us we were going camping in Hurley
So as quick as we could
We went on our way
Me, Jack, Amber and J.

Along by the river we saw a lama
Goats and sheep but no sign of a farmer.

We played football, volleyball
Mum said we can
Until we got told off by a grumpy old man.

We went to the shop to buy some food
Still thinking of the man
Who was terribly rude.

We went to bed
And had a fright
Which woke me up in the middle of the night.

Our short break is at the end
We all have had a great time
And I made a new friend.

Cara Waite (7)
Stoke Poges Primary School, Slough

Tests At School

The first important test I took
Was in Year 2, in a big blue book.
I didn't know so I wasn't scared,
I just sat on my chair and at my paper glared.

Verity Kyley (10)
Stoke Poges Primary School, Slough

My First Day At School

My first day at school I remember,
From my strict teacher I definitely did surrender.
When I walked home with my mum,
I felt a bit glum.
She then asked me was school fine,
Suddenly I said it was divine.
So on my next day at school,
I was pushed in the pool,
When I nearly drowned.
My teacher looked and frowned.
So when I came out
She did not shout,
I ran inside and tried to hide.
My teacher came to cheer me up,
She had brought some sweets in a cup,
And she said, 'Cheer up.'

Mishalle Iqbal (10)
Stoke Poges Primary School, Slough

Animals

The swan glides
The monkey hides
The bird chirps
The hippo burps
The rhino bathes
The hyena laughs
The seal claps
The cat naps
The lion roars
The dove soars.

Jasmine Jalif (10)
Stoke Poges Primary School, Slough

The Deadly Tiger

When you come across a tiger
You don't know what will happen next
You don't want to be alone
And there is nobody you can text.

Its eyes are as brown as wood
But it doesn't give out a purr
Its tail swishes and sways
As the tiger shows off its lovely fur.

When he starts stalking around you
You don't know what to do
You know you want to run away
Before it grabs hold of your shoe.

The tiger's tummy is rumbling
He roars and booms too
He can't find lunch anywhere
But he does like one thing on the menu
And that is you!

Baveena Heer (9)
Stoke Poges Primary School, Slough

Nature

Mother Nature what a beautiful thing,
Squirrels are dancing about,
Rabbits are hopping all over the place,
Trees are rustling gently.
Flowers and butterflies are there to admire ,
While the birds and bees fly around.
Rainbows sparkle and swirl.
Oh Mother Nature you're beautiful,
Oh Mother Nature you're grand.

Faye Bovington (8)
Stoke Poges Primary School, Slough

My Dad

My dad has so much care,
When I am lonely
He lets me sit in his comfy chair.

My dad is lovely and sweet,
When I do my homework
He takes a quick peep.

My dad gets annoyed when there is frost,
Because sometimes
He gets lost.

My dad loves us all,
Because when we were small
He taught us all how to crawl.

Aneesha Mahil (9)
Stoke Poges Primary School, Slough

My Family

My mum's number one,
She's great at cooking
And my best chum.

My dad's number two,
He's the best at sleeping
And loves the programme Boo!

Nathan's number three,
He's football crazy
And does not like bees.

Nash's number four,
He loves action toys
And sometimes is a bore.

Nikita Saggar (9)
Stoke Poges Primary School, Slough

My Dog Jessie

My dog's name is Jessie,
I found her as a stray.
Her hair is very scruffy,
And I'm not selling her, no way.

My dog's name is Jessie,
She's very obedient.
She runs around all day,
And she's happy and content.

My dog's name is Jessie,
She likes chasing sticks.
And when she's very happy,
She gives you sloppy licks.

My dog's name is Jessie,
She always eats her food.
She's the best dog in the world,
Even when she's in a mood.

Charlie Hertel (9)
Stoke Poges Primary School, Slough

My Pet

My pet has a tail,
My pet can purr,
It likes to run
And has lots of fur.
My pet has legs
And likes to sit on a mat.
For now you can guess
My pet is a . . .

Rabiah Khalid (9)
Stoke Poges Primary School, Slough

Happy And Sad

Sometimes I am happy
Sometimes I am sad
Sometimes I am crazy
Sometimes really mad

How can you make me happy?
How do you make me mad?
I really like laughing
But I hate being sad

How can you stop me?
You can't make me cry
Although I do sometimes
But I don't know why

Sometimes I fall over
And always cry a bit
When I have a shower
I cry, I lost my bath mit

This is how I do things
And that's what you do too
It always happens to me
But I don't know about you!

Aikta Sharma (9)
Stoke Poges Primary School, Slough

Patience

I have a young cousin called Keira
And every day I love her dearer and dearer
She's a handful at times
But like this poem, rhymes
I would miss her if she wasn't nearer.

Taylor Nelmes (7)
Stoke Poges Primary School, Slough

The Beach

The beach is my favourite place
where birds fly high in the sky
and where there is a lot to do.

The palm trees sway from side to side,
blocking the shining sun,
making shadows on the burning sand.

The waves are gentle and calm.
They crash gently against the rocks
creating small ripples to appear.
The whirlpools are full, making the fish come to life.

Children play in the sand
and use their imagination to create new lands.

When the tide comes in at the end of the day,
the beach becomes calm in every way.
The noise of people having fun
is overcome by crashing waves.

Ryan Lalli (7)
Stoke Poges Primary School, Slough

The Colour Blue

The colour blue reminds me of the deep blue sea.
The colour blue reminds me of the blue swimming pool.
The colour blue reminds me of the early morning blue sky.
The colour blue reminds me of fish fillet boxes.
The colour blue reminds me of the blue whale.
The colour blue reminds me of blu-tack.
The colour blue reminds me of the world map.

Amarjit Mann (10)
Stoke Poges Primary School, Slough

Terrier Tinsel

One snowy morning in a gust of hail
Terrier Tinsel went out to play
And wagged his fluffy tail.
A gale of snow came one day
On a Christmas Eve
Then it picked the puppy up
And blew him like a leaf.
Terrier Tinsel soon realised
That he was in the air
But when he saw he was higher than high
It gave him quite a scare.
The gale of snow soon had stopped
In the middle of some place
Terrier Tinsel had landed
With a sick kind of face.

Hannah Delderfield (9)
Stoke Poges Primary School, Slough

Snowflakes

Snowflakes come at Christmas,
Snowflakes are cold and white,
Snowflakes are soft and fluffy,
Snowflakes are wet and light!

Snowflakes are pointy,
Snowflakes are made from snow,
Snowflakes come in different patterns,
Snowflakes fall from high to low.

Snowflakes are pretty,
Snowflakes are fun,
I like snowflakes
But they soon melt in the sun!

Amy Benton (8)
Stoke Poges Primary School, Slough

Walking To School

Walking can be fun.
And you can look at leaves that
Look like trees.
Kicking conkers on the road.
Rustl Ing leaves in a pile.
   K Nocking conkers like Ashley Giles
Golden leaves that stretch for miles.

To gather leaves
On my way to school.

See cars whoosh past,
Count how many go fast.
Hopping over cracks on the pavement.
On the way we pass a garage.
Ooh there's a Zonda Dad, and a
Lamborghini!

Manraj Brar (8)
Stoke Poges Primary School, Slough

My Cat Misty

My feline friend, my purring pussy cat is a member of my family.
Misty is kind, loving and affectionate, just like a human.
Her fluffy fur is silky to touch like a satin pillow.
Her eyes sparkle like emeralds.
Her fur is as white as snow with patches of smoky grey clouds.
Her claws are as sharp as daggers.
Her tail swishes like a snake.
Misty can purr as loud as a lion and hiss like a snake.

Louise Pocock (9)
Stoke Poges Primary School, Slough

Two Of A Kind

My best friend is nice and funny
She plays with me
And she's always happy.

My best friend has a heart full of joy
Sometimes she gets upset
But she loves her cuddly toy,

For my best friend is someone
I'd contact from afar,
She's a nice, funny girl and her name's Aikta!

My other best friend is fun and cheeky
She laughs a ton
And I hate it when she's moany.

My best friend loves her bear Ted
I bet Ted loves sleeping
'Cause my friend has a four poster bed!

For my best friend is lovely
And really funny
She's someone who is joyful and that's Niki!

As you can see
They are two of a kind
They can be cross at times
Do you mind?

Malaika Kingue (9)
Stoke Poges Primary School, Slough

Tooth Fairy

I once saw a fairy
Her name was Mary
She fluttered around
Not making a sound
She left a coin under my pillow
And flew straight back to the willow.

Megan Picot (8)
Stoke Poges Primary School, Slough

My Two Cats

My two cats Calico and Bilbo
Are the sweetest cats in the world.
They are cute, loving and very kind.
Calico looks so beautiful, Bilbo looks so handsome.
If you see either of them you will suddenly go ahh!
Sometimes they are playful, sometimes they are mean
Because they're only kittens they fight every day.
When it comes to bedtime they sleep straight away.

Marianna Geany (9)
Stoke Poges Primary School, Slough

My Funny Mummy!

My mum has shiny eyes
They're as shiny as a sparkling car
Also my mum has lips like beautiful rosebuds
And has hair as beautiful as smooth wood
My mum's clothes are so cool
In fact, as cool as pop stars' clothes
When my mum gets angry she roars like a bear
But she's still the best mum!

Rebecca Holliday (9)
Stoke Poges Primary School, Slough

Seasons

In spring the flowers start to bloom
The morning sun comes into my room
In summer the sun is so bright,
I can hear the birds at first light.
In autumn the leaves fall down,
The trees are bare and everything's brown.
In winter the fields are white,
Children playing and having snow fights.

Simran Gill (8)
Stoke Poges Primary School, Slough

Aliens

I wonder if they're kind,
I wonder if they're blind,

> Do you imagine they are mean?
> Do you imagine they are green?

Do you think they are real?
Do you think they can heal?

> Can you imagine them crying?
> Can you imagine them lying?

Can you imagine them giving?
How long will they be living?

> Do you think they fight?
> Do you think they're light?

Harjoth S Bahra (10)
Stoke Poges Primary School, Slough

My Mum

My mum is sweet
my mum is nice
my mum is not ugly
and cuddles me every night.

She cares for me
and I care for her
we care for each other
and that is right.

I love my mum
and she loves me
she's the loveliest mum
there could ever be.

Laiqah Ramzan (7)
Stoke Poges Primary School, Slough

Night-Time Magic

Deep in the playroom the clock went tick-tock,
Then came the magic of 12 o'clock.
Dong! Dong! Dong! Dong!
For 12 beats the clock went on and on.
And then a quiet bawling started,
''Twas a baby who with her teddy'd been parted,
But no ordinary baby, a miniature one,
From the dolls' house on which the moonlight shone!
Then some tiny children picked up the tiddly teddy,
Put it in the cot and started to get ready,
As their mother had invited some guests round to stay,
And said they must look smart that day.
The guests came round and stayed for lunch,
They ate it up with a munch and a crunch,
And then (oh horror!) a child woke up,
Away the guests ran, forgetting to sup,
Mother froze, the kids ran to bed,
And the tiny little baby, clutched her little ted.

Gabrielle Bianco (8)
Woodcote Primary School, Woodcote

Butterfly Adventure

Here I go gliding through the breezy air
The big blue clouds are not so strong
As the sun bursts through them.

The beach was packed as I fluttered over
Oh what lovely sandcastles
'Argh!' I fell down into a hole.
I shouted for help and my brother came.
My wing was cut badly.
After a while on the beach my wing got better.
'Come on, my wing's much better now,
Let's go home.'

Bethany Smith (9)
Woodcote Primary School, Woodcote

A Sunday Walk

Me and Mum went to the woods
For our Sunday walk.

We heard some birds singing their songs
On our Sunday walk.

We watched the leaves play in the wind,
On our Sunday walk.

We smelt the toadstools and the mushrooms,
On our Sunday walk.

We felt the rough bark on the trees,
On our Sunday walk.

We got home in time for tea and toast,
After our Sunday walk.

Katie Thorne (7)
Woodcote Primary School, Woodcote

It's Autumn Because . . .

It's autumn because . . .
The squirrel has come again to collect her nuts.

It's autumn because . . .
The red and gold leaves are glowing on the ground
Like a bonfire, warm to stand around.

It's autumn because . . .
The heavy dew lays itself upon the spider's secret webs.

It's autumn because . . .
The bare branches of the trees
Look like skeletons standing alone to me.

Chloe Anderson (9)
Woodcote Primary School, Woodcote

Teachers Ooh No!

T eachers ooh no
E nter the school
A pile of school books in their hands.
C hildren running past the teachers
H earing what they say.
E nter their class line
R emembering to be quiet
S o then they can go into the class

O oooh no, the end of the day
O oooh no, the end of the day
H omework is coming

N o not today, Miss
O ffer us something else, Miss.

Anke-Katerina Andrews (10)
Woodcote Primary School, Woodcote

World War II

W icked things were happening.
O ver the world.
R inging air raid sirens.
L eaving families,
D ealing with injured people

W hen it was all over
A pplause all round,
R oars of happiness.

Emma Barrett (10)
Woodcote Primary School, Woodcote

Tom's Bomb

There once was a boy whose name was Tom
Who made a high explosive bomb
By mixing in some iodine
With water, sugar and plastercine.
Then to make it smell more queer
He added his daddy's home-made beer.
Tom mixed and mixed it together
And said his bomb would last forever.
Tom poured the mixture in a pot
Then stuck another on that lot,
Tom stuck a clock on its side
And decided he wanted to play on his slide.
Play and play and play did he,
Until he heard his brother scream,
'Tom come quickly, there is a bomb!'
Tom ran and ran,
As quick as a fan.
Through the door and up the stairs,
Over his sister's cuddly bears,
Then in his room there stood
His brother with no hood.
Although he should've guessed it before,
His brother's head was on the floor!
Tom said, 'It served him right to meet his doom,
He shouldn't have been in my room!'

Genevieve Simpson (9)
Woodcote Primary School, Woodcote

Lost Dog

I found a dog,
In a ditch.
He looked sad,
Abandoned.
He was in a cage.
I looked in his eyes
And saw freedom and living with a family.
I took him home and cleaned him up.
He found his destiny,
Now he's living with a family.

Kelly-Violet Draper (10)
Woodcote Primary School, Woodcote

Animals

A nimals are beautiful
N o one cares.
I love them.
M illions of animals
A ll kinds of animals
L ittle and big
S lowly vanishing.

Ellie Brown (9)
Woodcote Primary School, Woodcote

Blitz!

Blitz!
Fire in the air,
Bullets screaming across the sky,
Nazis flying, dropping bombs.
Buildings crashing down to Earth,
Towns on red, flaming fire.
Ordinary people being killed.
Planes crashing down.

Matthew Norman (10)
Woodcote Primary School, Woodcote

Elephant Circus

In an elephant circus
an elephant lay bored,
no fun, no laughter
or happiness in its cage.
It was sent from Africa to England
on purpose not by mistake.
Its owner is cruel
to make the elephant work hard,
but after a while it was sent to freedom,
back to Africa.
Now the sky is blue,
filled with a hot, shiny sun,
now the elephant is joyful with fun.

Baitong Namasonthi (9)
Woodcote Primary School, Woodcote